The clinical scenarios described in this book are entirely fictional. No resemblance to real people or actual cases is intended.

Every effort was made to ensure the accuracy of the material presented in this book at the time of publication.

Given that policies, procedures, and instructions can change at any time, candidates should always read and follow directions provided by the registering/licensing authority, the presiding officer, and the instructions contained in the Practical Nurse/Nursing Assistant Registration/Licensure Examination.

Candidates use the information, materials, and suggestions in this book at their own risk. Neither the Canadian Nurses Association nor its Testing Division assumes any responsibility for candidates' performance on the Practical Nurse/Nursing Assistant Registration/Licensure Examination.

2ND PRINTING OCTOBER, 1998
ISBN 1-55119-123-7   1ˢᵗ EDITION, 1995

Printed in Canada

TABLE OF CONTENTS

PREFACE

Congratulations! You have just purchased *The Canadian PN/NA Exam Prep Guide* to help you prepare for the Practical Nurse/Nursing Assistant Registration/Licensure Examination (PN/NA Exam). This guide is specially designed to familiarize you with the latest series of Canadian examinations that will be introduced in June 1996.

The Canadian PN/NA Exam Prep Guide is the only prep guide available that was created by the Canadian Nurses Association (CNA) Testing Division—the same group that develops and administers the PN/NA Exam in Canada. The knowledge and expertise of the professionals in this group make them the best qualified to produce a PN/NA Exam prep guide.

We have paid special attention to the format of the *Prep Guide* to ensure that it is user-friendly and flexible enough to accommodate students' different styles in preparing for the PN/NA Exam. We also give suggestions on how you can best use the *Prep Guide*, depending on the amount of time you have available before you write your PN/NA Exam. You can benefit from this *Prep Guide* whether you have several months or two weeks!

The *Prep Guide* is available in both English and French. We suggest that you select the guide that corresponds to the language of the examination you plan to write.

We would like to thank the many educators, administrators, and practical nurses/nursing assistants who contributed to the *Prep Guide*. As a result of their efforts, we are confident that this guide will be of great assistance to you as you prepare to write your examination.

Finally, our best wishes to you for success on the PN/NA Exam and throughout your nursing career.

G. R. Budgell

Glen R. Budgell, Ph.D.
Director of Testing
Canadian Nurses Association

Ottawa, Ontario
November 1995

Acknowledgments

The following people generously gave their time and expertise to the creation of *The Canadian PN/NA Exam Prep Guide.*

EXAM REVIEW PANEL

This panel consisted of five educators/administrators of practical nurses/nursing assistants from different locations and work settings in Canada. They reviewed the content of the Practice Exam and rationales—independently and as a group—to ensure the quality of these important *Prep Guide* components.

Caroline Churko
St. Boniface General Hospital
Winnipeg MB

Muriel Estey
London Board of Education
London ON

Dawn Kapler
Alberta Vocational College
Edmonton AB

Olive Noseworthy
Cabot Institute of Applied Arts,
    Technology and Continuing
    Education
St. John's NF

Judith Patterson
Minister of Education
Dartmouth NS

CONTENT REVIEW

The following educators, administrators, and practical nurses/nursing assistants participated in the content review process with the Practice Exam. This task involved a thorough review—either independently or as a group—of the items in the Practice Exam to ensure their consistency with current standards of practice in the representatives' province or territory.

Rita Abbott
St. Clare's Mercy Hospital
St. John's NF

Carolyn Allen
Yukon College
Whitehorse YK

Kay Barrington
Cabot Institute of Applied Arts,
    Technology and Continuing
    Education
St. John's NF

Nicole Beaudry
Collège Northern
Kapuskasing ON

Brent Bogart
Manitoba Association of
    Licensed Practical Nurses
Winnipeg MB

Angela Bonia
St. Pat's Mercy Home
St. John's NF

Elsie Boutillier
Professional Council of
    Registered Nursing Assistants
Edmonton AB

Denise Bowen
Aurora College
Yellowknife NT

Cathy Cameron
Sackville Hospital
Sackville NB

Darlene Chekay
Saskatchewan Institute of
    Applied Science and Technology
Regina SK

Lucille Chesser
New Brunswick Community
    College
Campbellton NB

Mary Clancy
Cambrian College
Sudbury ON

Walter Cole
Nova Scotia Community College
Yarmouth NS

Luisa Collela
St. Clair College
Windsor ON

Lorie Crawford
Aurora College
Yellowknife NT

Pat Dawson
Professional Council of
  Registered Nursing Assistants
Edmonton AB

Marilyn Delorme
Professional Council of
  Registered Nursing Assistants
Edmonton AB

Kim Diamond
Whitehorse General Hospital
Whitehorse YK

Sharon Dixon
East Kootenay Community
  College
Cranbrook BC

Janice Flemming
New Brunswick Community
  College
Saint John NB

Louise Frederick
Saskatchewan Institute of
  Applied Science and Technology
Regina SK

Norma Gaudet
New Brunswick Community
  College
Moncton NB

Irene Gendron
Manitoba Association of
  Licensed Practical Nurses
Winnipeg MB

Penny Gilson
Macauley Lodge
Whitehorse YK

Gisèle Guénard
Cambrian College
Sudbury ON

Bernice Hawkins
East Kootenay Community
  College
Cranbrook BC

Jean Hinchey
Whitehorse General Hospital
Whitehorse YK

Verna Holgate
Manitoba Association of
  Licensed Practical Nurses
Winnipeg MB

Cindy Hoyme
Professional Council of
  Registered Nursing Assistants
Edmonton AB

Lorraine Hoyt
Yukon College
Whitehorse YK

Jan Inman
Aurora College
Yellowknife NT

Susan Johnston
Assiniboine Community College
Brandon MB

Anne Keough
Council for Nursing Assistants
St. John's NF

Karen Kerrick
Sudbury Memorial Hospital
Sudbury ON

Joanne Labelle
Victorian Order of Nurses
Sudbury ON

Holly Lalonde
Saskatchewan Institute of
  Applied Science and Technology
Regina SK

Carole Lamothe
Cambrian College
Sudbury ON

Norm Larocque
Sudbury General Hospital
Sudbury ON

Patricia MacKenzie
Nova Scotia Community College
Sydney NS

Judy MacKinnon
Nova Scotia Community College
Bridgewater NS

Sheila McCabe
St. Clair College
Windsor ON

Normand McDonald
Association of New Brunswick
  Registered Nursing Assistants
Fredericton NB

Rosella McGrane
Saskatchewan Institute of
  Applied Science and Technology
Regina SK

Teresa Meng
Professional Council of
  Registered Nursing Assistants
Edmonton AB

Linda Patrick
St. Clair College
Windsor ON

Linda Robinson
Nova Scotia Community College
Dartmouth NS

Myrna Ross
Professional Council of
   Registered Nursing Assistants
Edmonton AB

Sandy Routliffe
St. Clair College
Windsor ON

Kathy Rovere
Malaspina University College
Nanaimo BC

Carolyn Sams
British Columbia Council of
   Licensed Practical Nurses
Burnaby BC

André Singfat
Assiniboine Community College
Brandon MB

Eileen St. Louis
Extendicare Falconbridge
   Nursing Home
Sudbury ON

Jean Trend
Central Newfoundland Regional
   College
Grand Falls NF

Mary Lou Trowell
Cambrian College
Sudbury ON

Colleen Turnbull
St. Clair College
Windsor ON

Lynn Van Montfoort
Okanagan University College
Kelowna BC

Marilyn Walsh
Presentation Convent
St. John's NF

Jane Weatherby
Professional Council of
   Registered Nursing Assistants
Edmonton AB

Dianne Westwood
Vancouver Community College
Vancouver BC

Ian Wheeler
Waterford Hospital
St. John's NF

Dorothy Windsor
Saskatchewan Institute of
   Applied Science and Technology
Regina SK

ITEM-WRITING COMMITTEE

The following educators, administrators, and practical nurses/nursing assistants participated in item-writing sessions, conducted in the fall and winter of 1994-95, at which questions and rationales were developed for the Practice Exam.

Fran Abbott
Cabot College of Applied Arts,
   Technology and Continuing
   Education
Registered Nursing Assistant
   Program
St. John's NF

Anne Bundgaard
Alberta Vocational College
Calgary AB

Mary Cammaert
Fanshawe College
London ON

Nora Carruthers
New Brunswick Department of
   Advanced Education and Labour
Moncton NB

Sharon Dixon
East Kootenay Community College
Cranbrook BC

Diana Ermel
Saskatchewan Institute of Applied
   Science and Technology
Regina SK

Muriel Estey
London Board of Education
London ON

Faye Feener
PEI School of Nursing
Summerside PE

Carl Gray
Confederation College
Thunder Bay ON

Helen Harrison
Assiniboine Community College
Brandon MB

Alice Howarth
Yukon College
Whitehorse YK

Sharon Jeffrey
George Brown College
Toronto ON

Dawn Kapler
Alberta Vocational College
Edmonton AB

Claudia Klymkiw
St. Boniface General Hospital
Winnipeg MB

Judy MacKinnon
Nova Scotia Community College
Bridgewater NS

Gail Maddox
Alberta Vocational College
Edmonton AB

Shirley A. McDonald
Professional Council of Licensed
    Practical Nurses
Edmonton AB

Gwen McLernon
New Brunswick Community
    College
Saint John NB

Marlene O'Connor
Northern College
South Porcupine ON

Judith A. Patterson
Minister of Education
Dartmouth NS

Judy Payne
Sheridan College
Mississauga ON

Judith Penney
Nova Scotia Community College
Sydney NS

Linda Vanginhoven
Uxbridge Cottage Hospital
Uxbridge ON

Norma Wildeman
Saskatchwan Institute of Applied
    Science and Technology
Regina SK

FRENCH REVIEWERS

The following educators and administrators participated in the review of the translation of the Practice Exam. This task involved a review of each question and rationale to ensure that the terminology used was consistent with current practice.

Lucille Chesser
Campbellton Community College
Campbellton NB

Norma Gaudet
New Brunswick Community
    College
Moncton NB

Linda Lepage-Leclair
Campbellton Community College
Campbellton NB

Gisèle L. Perrault
Hôpital général du Nipissing
ouest – Canadore College
North Bay ON

CNA STAFF

A number of CNA staff members contributed, in different ways, to the creation of *The Canadian PN/NA Exam Prep Guide*. These people included the members of the Core Team, who were responsible for planning and managing all of the activities related to the development of the *Prep Guide*, along with several individuals who were asked to assist with specific aspects of the project.

Core Team

Pierre Brochu
Maryse Céré
Martine Devaux
Amanda Joab
Johanne Killeen
Hugh Malcolm
Nadine Mathieu

Staff Contributors

Marie-Claude Bergeron
Françoise Boutet
John Braham
Carole Dazé
Eugène Duclos
Leslie Johnston
Yves Lafortune
Chantal Lafrenière
Natalie Lapointe
Josée Larivière-Asselin
Janice Newman-White
Mike Rannie
Michael Stein
Diane St-Pierre
Sonja Teige
Susan Ward

The CNA would also like to thank all the schools and colleges that took part in the experimental testing of some of the Practice Exam questions.

INTRODUCTION

The Canadian PN/NA Exam Prep Guide has been developed to assist candidates who will be writing the Practical Nurse/Nursing Assistant Registration/Licensure Examination (PN/NA Exam). This *Prep Guide* is designed specifically for candidates who plan to write the new series of examinations being introduced in June 1996.

Success on the PN/NA Exam depends on two main factors: (1) your knowledge of nursing principles and content, and (2) your ability to apply this knowledge, in the context of specific health care scenarios, on the PN/NA Exam.

This guide can help you in both areas. Completing the *Prep Guide* Practice Exam will help you review and integrate the concepts you have learned in your practical nurse/nursing assistant program; it will also help you assess your skill in applying that knowledge. The test instructions, test-taking strategies, and sample answer sheets can be used to enhance your readiness to write the PN/NA Exam. What better way to get ready than to gain practical experience by trying the practice questions in the *Prep Guide* and knowing what to expect on the PN/NA Exam!

The *Prep Guide* consists of several chapters designed to help you with different aspects of your preparation. In this chapter, you will learn the best way to use the *Prep Guide*, given your individual needs and the amount of time you have to prepare for the PN/NA Exam. Chapter 2 provides you with background information on the development, organization, and format of the PN/NA Exam. Chapter 3 contains a variety of general test-taking strategies, as well as specific strategies for answering multiple-choice questions. The Practice Exam is presented in Chapter 4. Chapter 5 explains how to use the answer keys to score the Practice Exam and describes how the actual PN/NA Exam is scored.

After checking your score on the Practice Exam against a score interpretation scale, you may wish to develop a Performance Profile—a self-evaluation of your strengths and weaknesses. Chapter 6 shows you how to create your Performance Profile. The rationales for each option in the Practice Exam are found in Chapter 7.

The Bibliography lists all of the references cited in the question rationales. Appendix A presents the list of competencies on which the PN/NA Exam is based. Addresses of the provincial and territorial registering/licensing authorities are provided in Appendix B. Appendix C contains a list of common abbreviations that appear on the Practice Exam and are likely to appear on the actual PN/NA Exam. At the back of the *Prep Guide*, you will find the Performance Profile Tally Sheet and Chart, four blank answer sheets for the Practice Exam, and a Satisfaction Survey. Your opinion is important to us, and we encourage you to send us your feedback in order that we may improve future editions of the *Prep Guide*.

BEFORE YOU BEGIN...

The *Prep Guide* is designed to familiarize you with the format of the actual PN/NA Exam and to provide you with information on the content of the examination. The PN/NA Exam is composed of three parts: Core Component, Medications Component, and Intravenous/Infusion Therapy Component. The Medications and Intravenous/Infusion Therapy Components are administered only in certain provinces and territories (i.e., only in provinces and territories in which the competencies measured by these components of the examination apply). Your registering/licensing authority can tell you if you are required to write the Medications or Intravenous/Infusion Therapy Component or both.

The Practice Exam contained in this book is a simulation of an actual PN/NA Exam. In the Core Component of the Practice Exam are 206 questions (two examination books, each containing 103 questions). The Medications and Intravenous/Infusion Therapy Components of the Practice Exam contain 21 and 20 questions respectively.

The questions presented in the Practice Exam are typical of those you will see on the actual PN/NA Exam. They represent common and predictable health situations of the population in those contexts or environments where beginning practical nurses/nursing assistants would work in a generalist role. As with the actual PN/NA Exam, the questions on the Practice Exam have been developed and reviewed by practical nurses/nursing assistants and educators of practical nurses/nursing assistants who represent a variety of educational programs, different clinical backgrounds, and different regions of the country. Furthermore, the Practice Exam has been designed according to the specifications and guidelines outlined in the *Blueprint for the Practical Nurse/Nursing Assistant Registration/ Licensure Examination* (1995), the document used to construct the actual PN/NA Exam. Hence, although the Practice Exam is not identical to the actual

PN/NA Exam that you will write, both examinations contain questions that measure specific competencies expected of practical nurses/nursing assistants beginning to practice in your province or territory.

One of the most important features of the *Prep Guide* is that, for each question on the Practice Exam, rationales are provided to explain why the options are correct or incorrect. These rationales emphasize nursing concepts and principles that are essential to beginning practical nurses/nursing assistants. For example, although the assessment questions and the communication questions on the *Prep Guide* Practice Exam are different from those on the actual PN/NA Exam, the general principles being tested are the same, because the questions are developed from the same set of competencies. Thus, by using the Practice Exam to review and reinforce the principles of client assessment and therapeutic communication, you will be better prepared to answer these types of questions on the actual PN/NA Exam.

Although your score on the Practice Exam can give you some indication of how prepared you are for the actual PN/NA Exam, it is important to note that the *Prep Guide* is only one aid to promote your success. The *Prep Guide* should be used to supplement and reinforce the knowledge and skills taught in your educational program.

Each question on the *Prep Guide* Practice Exam is supported by two references. Most of these references were published within five years of the *Prep Guide* publication date. The purpose of the references is twofold: to indicate that the correct answer within each of the questions has authoritative support from at least two experts in the field; and to provide you with a source for further reading and review. Every attempt has been made to use references that are up-to-date, accessible, and accepted within the profession. If you are unable to locate the specific references cited in the Bibliography, there are many other equally sound texts that provide support for the questions in the Practice Exam.

METHODS OF USING THE *PREP GUIDE*

The *Prep Guide* can be used in different ways depending on your particular needs and the amount of time you have before you write the PN/NA Exam. The three methods suggested below can be used independently, but they can also be used successively as part of a comprehensive study plan. Each method should be preceded by a review of Chapters 1, 2, and 3 before advancing to Chapter 4, *Taking the Practice Exam*. The three methods differ in approach based on the amount of time you have available before you write the actual PN/NA Exam. They cover periods of several months prior, one month prior, and two weeks prior to the actual PN/NA Exam.

METHOD A: IF YOU HAVE SEVERAL MONTHS BEFORE WRITING THE PN/NA EXAM

If you have several months before the examination, you may wish to write the complete Practice Exam under conditions that do not simulate the actual PN/NA Exam (e.g., do not be concerned with time limits; look ahead to a rationale to understand why a given answer is correct, before choosing your answer). Consider this process a dry run to familiarize yourself with the *Prep Guide* and the format and layout of the examination. In using this approach, work question-by-question without using the answer sheets. Answer one question and immediately check whether you selected the correct answer. Then read the rationales for the correct answer and the incorrect options to gain insight into what made you answer correctly or incorrectly.

This method will give you hands-on experience with multiple-choice questions and help you identify any difficulties you may have with the multiple-choice format (e.g., not picking up on key words in the question, making unwarranted assumptions, or reading too much into questions). On page 17, you will find a Checklist of Common Test-Taking Errors that will help you determine if you have particular difficulties with multiple-choice questions that can be corrected before writing the examination.

Since this method does not simulate actual examination conditions, we recommend that you do not calculate your total score or make any inferences based on your performance. However, shortly before taking the actual PN/NA Exam, you may benefit from taking the Practice Exam under actual examination conditions, as described in Method C.

METHOD B: IF YOU HAVE ONE MONTH BEFORE WRITING THE PN/NA EXAM

If you have approximately one month before the examination, you will want to more closely simulate actual examination conditions and still take advantage of a considerable amount of time in which to address any self-diagnosed weaknesses. With this method, complete the Practice Exam, either in its entirety or in discrete sections (e.g., a set of cases, a set of independent questions, or one examination book), before checking your answers against the answer key. Next, calculate your total score and interpret it according to the guidelines provided in Chapter 5. Then develop your Performance Profile to identify your strengths and weaknesses (see Chapter 6). The results of this self-diagnosis can then be used to identify gaps or deficiencies in your knowledge and skills. By knowing that you are weak in particular competency categories, for example, you can make your remaining study time more productive by concentrating on those specific areas. Studying for the PN/NA Exam will also be made easier by consulting the reference books linked to specific topics. You will find these references cited with the rationales for each question and listed in full in the Bibliography.

METHOD C: IF YOU HAVE TWO WEEKS BEFORE WRITING THE PN/NA EXAM

Method C is based upon a complete simulation of the actual examination. Follow the Practice Exam instructions precisely, time yourself, and use the answer sheets as if you were actually writing the PN/NA Exam. You can still benefit from creating your Performance Profile, as suggested in Method B. For the remaining study time, it may be most useful for you to concentrate on specific areas in which any weaknesses were identified. If you do not have time to obtain the references that correspond to your areas of weakness, you may prefer to concentrate on the rationales provided for each question in the Practice Exam.

Each province or territory in Canada is responsible for ensuring that all practical nurses/nursing assistants within its jurisdiction meet an acceptable level of competence before they begin to practice. This level of competence is measured by the Practical Nurse/Nursing Assistant Registration/Licensure Examination (PN/NA Exam) administered by all provincial and territorial registering/licensing authorities except Quebec's.*

The Canadian Nurses Association Testing (CNAT) Division has been developing the PN/NA Exam since 1971. The examination, offered in French and in English, has always been comprehensive in nature (i.e., integrates all clinical areas, such as obstetrics, pediatrics, etc.). The content and format of the examination, however, have been adapted over the years to meet the changing requirements for registration/licensure. The first administration of the newest series of the PN/NA Exam is in June 1996.

The examination is developed to measure an explicitly defined content area, which consists of the competencies expected of practical nurses/nursing assistants beginning to practice. These competencies, and the guidelines and specifications that outline the way they should be measured on the examination, are presented in the CNA's *Blueprint for the Practical Nurse/Nursing Assistant Registration/Licensure Examination* (1995).

A number of test development activities are carried out to produce the PN/NA Exam. Practical nurses/nursing assistants, educators and administrators from across Canada are included in all steps of the test development process, and their work is guided by CNAT staff to ensure that the PN/NA Exam meets the *Blueprint* guidelines and specifications. These test development activities include creation of examination questions, evaluation of questions to confirm that they reflect the current standards of practice across Canada, review of questions to ensure that they are fair and free of stereotypes, experimental testing of questions, and final approval of the questions by an examination committee before they appear on the PN/NA Exam. The Practice Exam has been developed in much the same manner as the actual PN/NA Exam.

---

* The registering/licensing authorities impose eligibility criteria, such as the completion of an approved practical nurse/nursing assistant educational program, which provide the added information required to decide on an individual's readiness to practice nursing.

WHAT IS TESTED WITH THE PN/NA EXAM

As mentioned earlier, the PN/NA Exam is composed of three parts: Core Component, Medications Component, and Intravenous/Infusion Therapy Component. The Medications and Intravenous/Infusion Therapy Components are administered only in certain provinces and territories (i.e., only in provinces and territories in which the competencies measured by these components of the examination apply). The content and specifications for the PN/NA Exam are described in the *Blueprint*. Summary Charts that outline the *Blueprint* specifications for examination development are presented on pages 10 to 12 for your reference. In Appendix A, you will find the complete list of 177 competencies that make up the content for the Core Component, as well as the competencies that make up the Medications (11) and Intravenous/Infusion Therapy (7) Components. Each question on the PN/NA Exam is linked to one of these competencies. The sections below provide brief explanations of the variables and guidelines referred to in the Summary Charts.*

COMPETENCIES

The first section of Summary Chart 1: Core Component of the PN/NA Exam—Development Guidelines shows that the list of competencies has been divided into four groups and that each group receives a different weight on the PN/NA Exam. The weights associated with these groups have been assigned to reflect the relative importance and frequency of the competencies in each group. Thus, competencies from Group A (high importance and frequency) will have the highest representation on the PN/NA Exam, while those from Group D (relatively low importance and frequency) will have the lowest representation. In Appendix A, the list of competencies for the Core Component of the

PN/NA Exam has been divided into these four groups. Because of the small number of competencies for the Medications and Intravenous/Infusion Therapy Components, no competency groupings were formed for these competencies.

STRUCTURAL VARIABLES

The general structure and appearance of the PN/NA Exam are determined by four structural variables: examination length and format, test equating, question presentation, and taxonomies of questions.

Examination Length and Format

The Core Component consists of 190 to 210 multiple-choice questions. The Medications Component and the Intravenous/Infusion Therapy Component each consist of 25 to 35 multiple-choice questions.

Test Equating

Test equating is done so that candidates will achieve the same examination result (pass or fail) regardless of the version of the examination they write (e.g., versions administered at different times). Test equating is accomplished by including a predetermined set of questions, known as anchor items, on all examination versions.

Question Presentation

The questions on the PN/NA Exam are presented as case-based (i.e., an introductory text followed by five or six questions) or independent questions (i.e., single questions unrelated to other questions). For the 190 to 210 questions on the Core Component, 60% to 70% are presented as independent questions, and 30% to 40% are presented within cases. The Medications and Intravenous/Infusion Therapy Components consist entirely of independent items.

---

* Some of the guidelines associated with the Core Component do not apply to the development of the Medications and Intravenous/Infusion Therapy Components. Where there are differences, these are specified.

Taxonomies: Cognitive and Affective Domains

Questions on the PN/NA Exam measure candidates' knowledge and abilities in nursing content across different levels of the cognitive domain. The three levels of cognitive ability reflected in the PN/NA Exam are Knowledge/Comprehension, Application, and Critical Thinking. As well, certain questions in the Core Component are designed to measure aspects of the affective domain. Questions in the Medications and Intravenous/Infusion Therapy Components are classified strictly within the cognitive domain. The cognitive and affective domains are defined below.

Cognitive Domain

Knowledge/Comprehension refers to the ability to recall previously learned material and to understand its meaning. It includes such mental abilities as knowing and understanding definitions, facts, and principles, and interpreting data (e.g., knowing the effects of certain procedures or interventions, understanding a change in a client's vital signs). Knowledge/Comprehension questions make up 20% to 30% of the Core Component, and 22% to 32% of the Medications and Intravenous/Infusion Therapy Components.

Application refers to the ability to apply knowledge to new or practical situations. It includes applying rules, methods, principles, and nursing theories in providing care to clients (e.g., applying diet therapy principles and concepts of comfort and safety to the nursing care of clients). Application questions make up 55% to 65% of the Core Component and 60% to 70% of the Medications and Intravenous/Infusion Therapy Components.

Critical Thinking refers to higher-level thinking processes. It includes the abilities to judge the relevance of data, to deal with abstractions, and to solve nursing problems (e.g., identifying priorities of care, evaluating the effectiveness of nursing actions). The practical nurse/nursing assistant should be able to identify cause-and-effect relationships, distinguish between relevant and irrelevant data, formulate valid conclusions, and make judgments concerning the needs of clients. The critical thinking level of the cognitive domain is represented by 5% to 10% of the questions on the Core Component, and 6% to 11% of the questions on the Medications and Intravenous/Infusion Therapy Components.

Affective Domain

The Core Component is also designed to assess competencies that involve attributes that do not strictly within the cognitive domain, such as attitudes and judgement. For the Core Component, the affective domain is characterized by the ability to examine one's own values when dealing with a client, a health situation, or the performance of nursing activities; the ability to react freely to these situations and to respond to them; the ability to become involved and to compare interests, attitudes, and opinions with those of colleagues or other members of the health care team; the ability to explain the client's situation and to interrelate different values presented; and the abilities to criticize conflicting situations with regard to health care, to identify one's professional limits, and to promote one's interests in the pursuit of education. A weight of 5% to 10% of the Core Component is assigned to questions reflecting the affective domain.

COMPETENCY CATEGORIES

For the purpose of the PN/NA Exam, the competencies have been classified into three major categories: Client Care, Communication Skills, and Professional and Personal Responsibilities (see diagram below). The Client Care category is further subdivided according to the steps of the nursing process: Assessment, Planning, Implementation, and Evaluation. Competencies are grouped into 16 subheadings under Implementation. The competencies for the Medications Component and the Intravenous/Infusion Therapy Component are classified as Client Care.

CONTEXTUAL VARIABLES

The following four variables set the context for the examination content:

Client Age and Gender

Specifications are provided for the age and gender of the clients described in the Core Component. The use of these variables ensures that the clients described in the examination represent the demographic characteristics of the Canadian population encountered by the practical nurse/nursing assistant beginning to practice. Client ages are categorized into three levels: child and adolescent (0–18 years); adult (19–64 years); and older adult (65+ years). Specifications for age and gender are not made for the Medications and Intravenous/Infusion Therapy Components because, often, the competencies can be measured without reference to a specific age or gender.

COMPETENCY CATEGORIES

1 CLIENT CARE

— *Assessment*
— *Planning*
— *Implementation*
    — Medications
    — Intravenous/ Infusion Therapy
— *Evaluation*

Admission, Discharge, & Transfer	Mobility
Asepsis, Wound Care, & Infection Control	Nutrition
Death	Personal Hygiene
Devices & Equipment	Preoperative & Postoperative Care
Drainage, Irrigation, & Suctioning	Respiration & Ventilation
Elimination	Safety & Comfort
Emergency Care	Specimen Collection & Diagnostic Testing
Maternal, & Child Care	Teaching & Education

2 COMMUNICATION SKILLS

3 PROFESSIONAL & PERSONAL RESPONSIBILITIES

Client Culture

Some of the questions on the PN/NA Exam have been included to measure awareness, sensitivity, and respect for different cultures within Canada. Cultural issues are integrated within the examination without introducing cultural stereotypes.

Client Health Situation

Various client health situations are represented on the PN/NA Exam. These situations are developed from a nursing focus and reflect different combinations of the following elements: (a) client dimensions (i.e., biophysical, psychosocial, spiritual), (b) care for clients throughout the life cycle, and (c) application of the nursing process.

Health Care Environment

Because practical nurses/nursing assistants are prepared to work in a variety of settings and contexts, and most of the competencies are not setting-dependent, questions on the PN/NA Exam are set within particular health care environments only when required for clarity.

HOW THE PN/NA EXAM IS ORGANIZED

The PN/NA Exam is divided into four books: two books for the Core Component and one book each for the Medications and Intravenous/Infusion Therapy Components. Some candidates will write only the Core Component, others will write the Core and Medications Components, and yet others will write the Core, Medications, and Intravenous/Infusion Therapy Components. The components you must write are determined by the licensing authority in your province or territory. The PN/NA Exam is administered over the course of one day.

Each question on the examination, whether in the case-based or independent format, contains a stem and four options. The stem is typically made up of one to three sentences that provide relevant information or data and the specific nursing question that is being asked. Of the four options, one is the correct or best answer and the remaining three are incorrect or less correct options.

Some of the questions in each examination book are *experimental*. That is, they are being tried to determine their suitability for use on future exams. Although your answers to these experimental questions do not count toward your score, it is important to do your best on each question on the examination because you have no way of knowing which questions are experimental.

You will find examples of the type of questions used in the actual PN/NA Exam in Chapter 4, *Taking the Practice Exam*.

SUMMARY CHART 1: CORE COMPONENT OF THE PN/NA EXAM—DEVELOPMENT GUIDELINES

COMPETENCIES

Group A: 75–80% of questions	Group B: 10–20% of questions	Group C: 5–15% of questions	Group D: 1–10% of questions

STRUCTURAL VARIABLES

Examination Length and Format	190–210 objective questions (e.g., multiple-choice)
Test Equating	Anchor items are used to accomplish test equating.
Question Presentation	60–70% independent questions 30–40% case-based questions
Taxonomies for Questions Cognitive Domain	Knowledge/Comprehension: 20–30% of questions Application: 55–65% of questions Critical Thinking: 5–10% of questions
Affective Domain	5–10% of questions

CONTEXTUAL VARIABLES

Client Age and Gender	**Male** **Female** 0 to 18 years 12–15% 12–15% 19 to 64 years 14–23% 15–24% 65+ years 12–18% 17–23%
Client Culture	Questions will be included that measure awareness, sensitivity, and respect for different cultural values, beliefs, and practices, without introducing stereotypes.

Client Health Situation	Using the contextual variables, the elements below are applied in different combinations to develop a *cross section* of questions:
	
	A. Biophysical
	  Psychosocial
	  Spiritual
	
	B. Care for clients throughout the life cycle
	
	C. Application of the nursing process

Health Care Environment	The health care environment is specified *only* where necessary.

SUMMARY CHART 2: MEDICATIONS COMPONENT OF THE PN/NA EXAM—DEVELOPMENT GUIDELINES

COMPETENCIES

The 11 Medications competencies are given approximately equal weight, with the final distribution of questions established by the Examination Committee representatives of the user jurisdictions.

STRUCTURAL VARIABLES

Examination Length and Format	25–35 objective questions (e.g., multiple-choice)
Test Equating	Anchor items are used to accomplish test equating.
Question Presentation	Independent questions
Taxonomies for Questions Cognitive Domain	Knowledge/Comprehension: 22–32% of questions Application: 60–70% of questions Critical Thinking: 6–11% of questions

CONTEXTUAL VARIABLES

Client Age and Gender	There are no explicit specifications for client age and gender on the Medications Component of the examination.
Client Culture	Questions will be included that measure awareness, sensitivity, and respect for different cultural values, beliefs, and practices, without introducing stereotypes.
Client Health Situation	Using the contextual variables, the elements below are applied in different combinations to develop a *cross section* of questions: A. Biophysical Psychosocial Spiritual B. Care for clients throughout the life cycle C. Application of the nursing process
Health Care Environment	The health care environment is specified *only* where necessary.

SUMMARY CHART 3: INTRAVENOUS/INFUSION THERAPY COMPONENT OF THE PN/NA EXAM —DEVELOPMENT GUIDELINES

COMPETENCIES

The seven Intravenous/Infusion Therapy competencies are given approximately equal weight, with the final distribution of questions established by the Examination Committee representatives of the user jurisdictions.

STRUCTURAL VARIABLES

Examination Length and Format	25–35 objective questions (e.g., multiple-choice)
Test Equating	Anchor items are used to accomplish test equating.
Question Presentation	Independent questions
Taxonomies for Questions Cognitive Domain	Knowledge/Comprehension: 22–32% of questions Application: 60–70% of questions Critical Thinking: 6–11% of questions

CONTEXTUAL VARIABLES

Client Age and Gender	There are no explicit specifications for client age and gender on the Intravenous/Infusion Therapy Component of the examination.
Client Culture	Questions will be included that measure awareness, sensitivity, and respect for different cultural values, beliefs, and practices, without introducing stereotypes.
Client Health Situation	Using the contextual variables, the elements below are applied in different combinations to develop a *cross section* of questions: A. Biophysical 　Psychosocial 　Spiritual B. Care for clients throughout the life cycle C. Application of the nursing process
Health Care Environment	The health care environment is specified *only* where necessary.

Test-Taking Strategies

3

This chapter will help you prepare to write the PN/NA Exam by reviewing what you need to do before and during the examination, what to bring to the examination centre, and how to optimize your performance on multiple-choice questions.

BEFORE THE PN/NA EXAM

■ *Arrange to Write the PN/NA Exam*

If you are interested in writing the PN/NA Exam, you must arrange to do so by contacting the registering/licensing authority in the province or territory in which you wish to write. Their staff will inform you of the documentation you must provide to register for the examination as well as the fee you will have to pay. The list of registering/licensing authorities that use the PN/NA Exam is presented in Appendix B.

All candidates are entitled to receive a fair and valid assessment. Therefore, CNAT, in conjunction with the registering/licensing authorities, will authorize reasonable and appropriate modifications to the PN/NA Exam administration procedures to accommodate candidates with disabilities. For further information, contact your registering/licensing authority.

■ *Read* The Canadian PN/NA Exam Prep Guide

The *Prep Guide* contains information that will help you become more familiar with the PN/NA Exam. The rationales for the correct answers (and the incorrect options) and the references listed in the Bibliography provide ideal resources to review essential nursing content. You are also presented with a variety of ways to use the *Prep Guide*, depending on how much time you have before you write the PN/NA Exam.

■ *Take the Practice Exam in the Prep Guide*

Taking the Practice Exam under conditions that are as close as possible to those of the actual PN/NA Exam is an effective way to prepare and to ensure that there will be no surprises. Give yourself the right amount of time to complete each examination book and do not look ahead to the answers. To simulate true examination conditions, arrange to take the Practice Exam with other students who are also interested in preparing for the examination.

■ *Use the Information from Your Performance Profile*

By conducting an analysis of your performance on the Practice Exam, you will be able to identify your strengths and weaknesses. Use this information to your advantage to focus your studying in areas of weakness. Details on how to create your Performance Profile are found in Chapter 6.

■ *Study Effectively*

Select a place that is quiet and free from distractions, yet comfortable for studying. Develop a study plan, dividing your time between specific topics or sections. Keep in mind that five 2-hour sessions are likely to be more beneficial than two 5-hour sessions. Monitor your progress and revise your schedule as necessary.

■ *Prepare for the Examination Day*

Check the location of the examination centre and examination room and determine how much time you will need to get there. If necessary, do a practice run and confirm bus schedules or the availability of parking. As well, it is important to be alert and focused when you write the examination—be sure to get plenty of rest the night before the examination and to eat a suitable breakfast before you arrive at the examination centre.

WHAT TO BRING TO THE PN/NA EXAM

■ *Identification*

In most cases, you must bring your candidate identification card, issued by your registering/licensing authority. They will also inform you whether you are required to present additional identification.

■ *Pencils/Eraser*

Unless otherwise advised, take two or three medium-soft (HB) pencils and a soft pencil eraser.

■ *Watch*

Each examination room should have a clock, and you will be periodically advised of the time remaining to complete the examination. However, you might want to bring a watch to keep closer track of the time and to gauge your pace.

WHAT NOT TO BRING

Books, paper, notes, calculators, and other aids are not permitted in the examination room.

WHAT TO WEAR

Remember that you will be sitting for hours. Wear comfortable clothing.

DURING THE PN/NA EXAM

■ *Listen to All Announcements*

The examination administrator will inform you of important details, such as how long you have to complete the examination and how and where to hand in your examination book and answer sheet, as well as when you should arrive for the next session.

■ *Read the Examination Book Instructions*

Examination instructions are very important. It is essential that you have a clear understanding of what you are expected to do. If you do not understand what you have been told or what you have read, ask questions in the period before the examination officially begins.

■ *Complete All Information Accurately*

You will be required to fill in certain information on your answer sheets and examination books (e.g., your candidate number from your identification card). Errors made in completing this information can delay the scoring of your examination. If you make errors in recording your choice of answer on one or more examination questions, you will not be given any credit for those questions. For each question, be sure to record a single answer in the appropriate place on the answer sheet.

■ *Read the Question Carefully*

Concentrate on what is being asked in the question and relate it to the data provided. Do not make any assumptions unless they are directly implied.

Pick out important words that relate to the question. For example, in some questions you may be asked for the *most appropriate initial response* by the practical nurse/nursing assistant, but you should be aware that questions that follow may deal with the *most appropriate measure* by the practical nurse/nursing assistant or the *most appropriate intervention* by the practical nurse/nursing assistant. Reviewing the questions in the Practice Exam will help you to recognize key words that will appear on the PN/NA Exam.

■ *Do One Question at a Time*

Consider each question a separate entity. Do not let a difficult question make you anxious as you approach the next one. Do the best you can with each question and move on to the next. Try not to rush, but do not spend more than two or three minutes on any individual question. If you do not know the answer, skip the question and return to it later. Something in a subsequent case or question might jog your memory. If you still do not know the answer, do not be afraid to guess; no points are deducted for wrong answers. If you do not answer all the questions in sequence, it is particularly important to ensure that the oval you are filling in on your answer sheet is aligned with the correct question number.

When you decide on a correct answer from among the options, immediately indicate your choice on the answer sheet before moving on to the next question. Do not circle all the answers in the examination book and transfer them when you are finished the book because you could run out of time, and credit is not given for answers in your examination book—only for answers recorded on your answer sheet.

■ *Changing Your Answer*

If you decide to change an answer after filling it in on your answer sheet, make sure the original choice is completely erased. Otherwise, it will appear as though you have selected two options. This will be scored as an incorrect answer. Similarly, avoid making stray marks on your answer sheet that the computer could inadvertently pick up as answers to questions.

Be cautious about changing your answer. Very often your first choice is correct. Making a new selection is advantageous only if you are confident that the new option is correct.

■ *Guessing*

There is no penalty for guessing on the PN/NA Exam. You will not lose any marks if you select an incorrect answer.

STRATEGIES FOR MULTIPLE-CHOICE QUESTIONS

■ *Familiarize Yourself with Multiple-Choice Questions*

A thorough understanding of multiple-choice questions will allow you to apply your nursing knowledge and skills to the testing situation most effectively. A multiple-choice question is constructed so that only someone who has mastered the subject matter will select the correct answer; to that person, only one option appears to be the correct answer. To someone who lacks a firm grasp of the subject matter, all options may seem plausible.

■ *Use a Three-Step Approach*

It is often helpful to use the following three-step approach to answer the multiple-choice questions that appear on the PN/NA Exam:

1. Carefully read the information provided in the case text (for cases) and in the question. Try to understand the client's health situation and the nursing care the client is likely to require.

2. Before looking at the options, make sure you have understood the question. Use the information provided and, based on your nursing knowledge and skills, try to imagine the correct answer.

3. Study the alternatives provided and select the one that comes closest to the answer you imagined. You may wish to reread the question before finalizing your selection.

■ *Take Advantage of the Process of Elimination*

If you are not presented with an option that matches or is close to the one you imagined after reading the question, try to eliminate some of the options that are absolutely incorrect. The following example illustrates how you can benefit from the process of elimination.

EXAMPLE QUESTION

Which one of the following responses by the practical nurse/nursing assistant would best assist Mr. Jones to verbalize his fears when he expresses anxiety about the possibility of having surgery?

1. "I know exactly how you feel about this."
2. "Would you like to talk to the nurse-in-charge?"
3. "You seem worried that you may need to have surgery."
4. "It's a normal reaction to be afraid when faced with surgery."

To take full advantage of the process of elimination, it is important to focus on the key idea in the question. The key idea is *assisting the client to verbalize his fears*. In Option 1, the spotlight is on the practical nurse/nursing assistant and not on the client or his concerns. Option 1 can be eliminated because it is highly unlikely that any one person knows exactly how someone else feels in a given situation.

Option 2 also fails to address the client's immediate concern because the practical nurse/nursing assistant completely avoids dealing with the client and passes the responsibility on to another team member. For this reason, Option 2 can be eliminated as a possible correct answer.

Option 4 should also be eliminated. By telling the client that what he is experiencing is "normal," the practical nurse/nursing assistant implies that the client's situation is routine. Such a response would be depersonalizing and nontherapeutic.

After these three options are systematically eliminated, you can consider Option 3, the correct option, which is open-ended and encourages the client to begin talking about how he feels about his approaching surgery.

CHECKLIST OF COMMON TEST-TAKING ERRORS

Students often make mistakes on an examination because of errors in processing facts and information or because of problems in answering multiple-choice questions. These are technical errors related to writing tests and not to a lack of nursing knowledge or skills.

As you proceed through the Practice Exam and determine whether you answered questions correctly, you may wish to keep a checklist of problems you had related to your test-taking skills. You can then use the results of this checklist to identify skills that you need to develop during your preparation for the PN/NA Exam.

A Checklist of Common Test-Taking Errors is provided on page 17. Some of the most common errors are listed in the left-hand column. Tick off the particular technical error(s) you made with the questions you answered incorrectly. Keep in mind that you may have more than one technical error with any one question.

CHECKLIST OF COMMON TEST-TAKING ERRORS

Missed important information in the case text	
Misread the question	
Failed to pick out important or key words in the question	
Did not relate the question to information in the case text	
Made assumptions in reading the case text or question	
Focused on insignificant details and missed key issues	
Selected more than one answer	
Incorrectly transferred answer from selection in examination book to answer sheet	
Switched answer selected to an incorrect response	

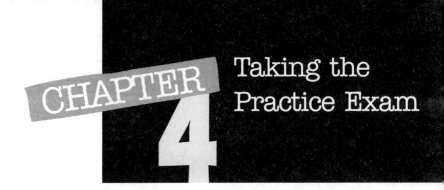

The Practice Exam is divided into 4 books. Book 1 and Book 2 contain the questions of the Core Component, Book 3 is the Medications Component, and Book 4 is the Intravenous/Infusion Therapy Component. As on the actual PN/NA Exam, you should complete only those components of the Practice Exam that are required by your registering/licensing authority. How you complete the Practice Exam will depend on whether you are using Method A, B, or C (described in Chapter 1). If you are going to take the Practice Exam only once, gain the maximum benefit from this experience by attempting to simulate the actual examination conditions as closely as possible. That means writing the examination in a quiet location, without the benefit of books, notes, or other aids, and strictly adhering to the time limits.

Since there are no experimental questions* being tested on the Practice Exam (i.e., all the questions that you complete will count toward your total score), you should limit yourself to 2 hours and 15 minutes for each examination book in the Core Component. If you are writing the Medications or Intravenous/Infusion Therapy Components or both, limit yourself to 30 minutes for each examination book. Experimental questions are included in the examination books of the actual PN/NA Exam. Therefore, you will be allowed more time per book.

The covers of the Practice Exam and the instructions are similar to those on the PN/NA Exam, except that the administration time limits differ in the instructions for the actual PN/NA Exam. Read these instructions carefully, but keep in mind that during your simulation you will not have the benefit of a presiding officer to remind you of how much time is remaining. On the cover of each Practice Exam book is a *test form number* that is also repeated in the lower left-hand corner of each page of the examination book. This test form number is used by the Canadian Nurses Association for scoring the actual PN/NA Exam.

Blank answer sheets are included with the *Prep Guide* (see *Additional Materials* section) in order that you can gain experience in recording the personal information and filling in the ovals that correspond to your answer selections. Familiarize yourself with the candidate information you will be required to complete when you write the PN/NA Exam.

You should wait until you have finished the entire Practice Exam to calculate your total score and to create your Performance Profile. The information will be complete and, therefore, more accurate and more useful to you. Instructions on calculating your score and determining your Performance Profile are provided in Chapters 5 and 6.

---

* Experimental questions are questions being tested for future use; they do not count toward the examination score.

CANADIAN NURSES ASSOCIATION

TESTING DIVISION

PRACTICAL NURSE/NURSING ASSISTANT
REGISTRATION/LICENSURE EXAMINATION

CANDIDATE NUMBER

SIGNATURE

BOOK 1
TEST FORM 9996

READ THE INSTRUCTIONS AND SAMPLE QUESTIONS INSIDE THE FRONT COVER

CANADIAN NURSES ASSOCIATION
ASSOCIATION DES INFIRMIÈRES ET INFIRMIERS DU CANADA

21

INSTRUCTIONS

A) TESTING TIME AND MATERIAL

You will have two hours and 15 minutes to work on this test book. The starting and finishing times will be announced and you will be advised when there are 30 and 15 minutes working time remaining. If at any time you have any questions about what you should do, raise your hand and an invigilator will assist you.

You will be advised whether you may leave the examination room if you finish the test book before the time is up. You must **stop** working when the signal is given. An invigilator will check your test book and answer sheet **before** you leave.

Clear your desk of all materials except your identification card, answer sheet, test book, pencils, and eraser. **Do not** fold, bend, or tear your answer sheet, as this could affect the scoring of your test.

B) ANSWER SHEET

Write your name, date of birth, date of writing, and test title in the corresponding boxes. Enter in your CANDIDATE NUMBER, the WRITING CENTRE CODE, and the TEST FORM and fill in the corresponding ovals. If you do not have a candidate number leave this section blank. Complete the box labeled LANGUAGE OF WRITING.

Be sure the mark you make for each answer is black, fills the oval, and contains the number corresponding to the number of the answer you have chosen. Do **not** fill in more than one oval for a question or you will not get credit for it. Erase **completely** any answer you wish to change and mark your new choice in the correct oval. An incomplete erasure may be read incorrectly as an intended answer. Do not press too heavily on your pencil or you may damage the answer sheet.

Note that the questions on the answer sheet are numbered in columns. There are fewer questions in the test book than there are numbers on the answer sheet.

Make no stray marks on the answer sheet; they may count against you. You may use the margins of the test book for any scratch work, but you will **not** get credit for anything you write in the test book.

C) TEST BOOK

Sign your name on the line on the cover of this book and copy your candidate number into the appropriate boxes. If you do not have a candidate number, **print** your name under your signature.

Read each question carefully and choose the answer you think is **correct**. If you cannot decide on an answer to a question, go on to the next one and come back to this question later if you have time. Try to answer all questions. Marks are not subtracted for wrong answers. If you are not sure of an answer, it will be to your advantage to guess. It will probably be best to start at the beginning of the test book and work through the questions in order.

This examination contains a number of experimental questions being tested for future use. Your answers to these questions will **not** count toward your score. Because you will not be able to tell which questions are experimental, you should do your best on all questions, but **do not** spend too much time on any question.

The questions in the examination may be presented in cases or as independent questions. The context of some cases may seem similar to others in your test book. This reflects current practice where a practical nurse/nursing assistant may have to care for different clients with similar problems. Each case, however, tests different nursing content. The sample case on the next page shows the type of questions used. Correct answers are blackened in the ovals on the right.

SAMPLE CASE

Mr. Martin, 68 years old, is admitted to hospital with a diagnosis of pneumonia. The physician's orders include bedrest, oxygen therapy by mask, and incentive spirometer q. 1–2 h.

QUESTIONS 1 to 4 refer to this case.

1. Mr. Martin becomes upset when he learns he must stay in bed. Which one of the following approaches should the practical nurse/nursing assistant use when establishing a rapport with Mr. Martin?

    1. "Hello, Mr. Martin. I will be caring for you today and I am here to see that you follow the physician's orders."
    2. "Good morning, Mr. Martin. I hear you are unhappy about being put on bedrest."
    3. "Good morning, Mr. Martin. I understand you are upset about being on bedrest, but it's only for a few days."
    4. "Hello, Mr. Martin. I understand you have been put on bedrest. How do you feel about that?"

2. Mr. Martin is receiving oxygen as ordered. While changing his bed, the practical nurse/nursing assistant notices that the television has a frayed wire. Which one of the following actions should the practical nurse/nursing assistant take immediately?

    1. Turn off the oxygen and report the situation.
    2. Turn off and unplug the television, attach a "do not use" sign, and report the situation.
    3. Make arrangements to have Mr. Martin's television exchanged for one in safe working order.
    4. Caution Mr. Martin not to use the television until someone checks it.

3. The practical nurse/nursing assistant has been asked to assist Mr. Martin with his breathing and coughing exercises. Which one of the following actions should the practical nurse/nursing assistant take to promote his performance?

    1. Encourage Mr. Martin to inhale slowly and exhale rapidly.
    2. Instruct Mr. Martin to use his spirometer every hour.
    3. Ensure Mr. Martin is in a supine position when performing his breathing exercises.
    4. Explain to Mr. Martin that the best time to cough up secretions is in the evening before going to sleep.

4. Which one of the following actions should the practical nurse/nursing assistant implement when providing mouth care for Mr. Martin?

    1. Ensure oral hygiene is completed every 2–3 hours.
    2. Wear sterile gloves.
    3. Provide mouthwash at the bedside.
    4. Keep the humidifier bottle filled with normal saline. ①②③④

END OF SAMPLE CASE

DO NOT GO TO THE NEXT PAGE OR BEGIN WORKING UNTIL THE SIGNAL IS GIVEN TO DO SO

CASE 1

Samantha Stevens, a 16-year-old high school student, is severely dehydrated after experiencing diarrhea for the past 3 days. She has been admitted to a pediatric unit at a local hospital and has been placed on enteric precautions.

QUESTIONS 1 to 6 refer to this case.

1. Which one of the following measures by the practical nurse/nursing assistant is essential to ensure that enteric precautions are maintained for Samantha?
   1. Wear a mask and gloves when entering Samantha's room.
   2. Ensure that everyone entering Samantha's room wears a gown and gloves.
   3. Remind Samantha that she must remain in her room at all times.
   4. Wear a gown and gloves when handling articles soiled with fecal material.

2. The physician has ordered a stool specimen for ova and parasites to be collected from Samantha. What special measures must be taken by the practical nurse/nursing assistant to ensure that Samantha's stool specimen is collected correctly?
   1. Collect the specimen in a dry container.
   2. Collect a specimen in the appropriate container.
   3. Collect the specimen in a sterile container.
   4. Collect a swab of the stool specimen.

3. After designing a plan of care with input from Samantha, the practical nurse/nursing assistant finds her uncooperative. Which one of the following approaches by the practical nurse/nursing assistant would most likely foster Samantha's participation in her plan of care?
   1. Remind Samantha that following the plan will result in an early discharge, allowing her to be back at school with her friends sooner.
   2. Encourage Samantha to record her own fluid intake, urinary output, and bowel movements on the fluid balance record.
   3. Encourage Samantha to complete her personal care before lunch so she will have time for a nap before her friends arrive.
   4. Remind Samantha in a gentle manner that she has to wash her hands after using the washroom and before meals.

A9-9996

4. Samantha has developed a rash around her rectum for which she is applying barrier cream. Which one of the following statements by the practical nurse/nursing assistant to Samantha indicates that the practical nurse/nursing assistant is using the evaluation phase of the nursing process?

1. "Do you have enough barrier cream left to apply to your rectal area?"
2. "It looks like the area around your rectum is healing. Does it feel better?"
3. "Tell me when you've finished your bath so that rectal cream can be applied."
4. "Remember to wash your rectal area after each bowel movement and to apply rectal cream."

5. Samantha is expecting her friends to visit in the afternoon. She is quite concerned about her appearance as she has been too weak to shampoo her hair since she was admitted 2 days ago. How should the practical nurse/nursing assistant assist Samantha to get ready for her visitors?

1. Help her to the shower on the unit and ensure that a bath chair is available.
2. Shampoo her hair by placing her on a stretcher at the sink in her room.
3. Assist her to shampoo her hair while seated at the sink in her bathroom.
4. Postpone the shampoo and help her to style her hair.

6. As Samantha's condition improves, she spends all her time watching television alone. Which one of the following diversionary activities should the practical nurse/nursing assistant suggest as an alternative?

1. That Samantha's parents visit every day to lessen her loneliness
2. That Samantha ask a couple of friends to visit so they can talk about what is happening at school
3. That Samantha assist the activity worker with the children in the playroom
4. That Samantha's friends drop off her homework so that she will have caught up when she returns to school

END OF CASE 1

CASE 2

[handwritten: Client often lean on elbows to change position]

Sam Young, 32 years old, fractured his left femur last evening. He was admitted from the operating room, where he had a pin inserted through his distal left femur, and was placed in skeletal traction. His bed is equipped with an overbed trapeze.

[handwritten: foot roll: must maintain the line of pull]

QUESTIONS 7 to 12 refer to this case.

7. When assessing Sam's pin insertion sites, which one of the following findings must the practical nurse/nursing assistant report to the nurse-in-charge immediately?

   [handwritten: inflammed skin edges]

   1. Non-irritated skin edges with sero-sanguineous drainage
   2. Dark red skin edges with serous drainage
   3. Puffy skin edges without drainage
   4. Pink skin edges with dry sanguineous drainage

8. Which one of the following rationales demonstrates that the practical nurse/nursing assistant understands why sheepskin protectors have been applied to Sam's elbows?

   [handwritten: they absorb moisture, prevent skin breakdown]

   1. To reduce friction on the elbows
   2. To prevent constriction of vessels at the elbows
   3. To lower the possibility of nerve damage at the elbows
   4. To keep the skin soft and moist on the elbows

9. Which one of the following activities as ordered by the physician would best help Sam maintain his muscle strength while he is in traction?

   [handwritten: ↑ muscle tension by applying pressure against stable resistance; opposing adjacent muscles in the eg press hands together pinch/pull against immovable object; joint movt, length of muscle unchanged / muscle strength/tone maintained/improved]

   1. Isometric exercises to his affected leg several times daily
   2. Passive range-of-motion exercises to his upper body several times daily
   3. Deep breathing and coughing exercises several times daily
   4. Isotonic exercises to his affected leg several times daily

10. Which one of the following instructions should the practical nurse/nursing assistant give Sam to obtain his assistance while removing and replacing the sheets on his bed?

    1. Roll laterally in a gentle motion. *[handwritten: Roll is contraindicated in traction]*
    2. Use the trapeze to lift his body. *[handwritten: can maintain the line of pull]*
    3. Use the side rails for support.
    4. Slide toward the foot of the bed. *[handwritten: alter angle of traction]*

11. The practical nurse/nursing assistant assesses Sam's back and finds areas that are constantly red from the pressure of lying on them. Which one of the following actions should the practical nurse/nursing assistant provide to prevent pressure sore formation?
    1. Rub the red areas well with emollient cream. *further tissue damage*
    2. Massage the red areas gently with alcohol.
    3. Massage the back around the red areas.
    4. Rub around the red areas with alcohol. *cause further tissue damage as area is red*

12. Where should the practical nurse/nursing assistant attach Sam's call bell to ensure that it remains most readily accessible to him?
    1. Bedside table
    2. Headboard
    3. Side rail
    4. Trapeze bar *accessible within field of vision*

END OF CASE 2

CASE 3

Mrs. Smith, 64 years old, has been on a medical unit recovering from a myocardial infarction. Upon arriving in Mrs. Smith's room to provide morning care, the practical nurse/nursing assistant discovers that her condition has changed.

QUESTIONS 13 to 18 refer to this case.

13. Which one of the following assessments would best indicate to the practical nurse/nursing assistant that Mrs. Smith's health status has deteriorated and that her condition must be reported immediately?
    1. Cold, clammy skin
    2. Full, bounding pulse *thready pulse*
    3. Elevated blood pressure
    4. Increased muscular activity

cardiogenic shock:
• cold clammy skin
• rapid thready pulse
• hypotension
• ↓ blood flow ⇒ lethargy

27

regularity, rhythm

14. While assessing Mrs. Smith's radial pulse, the practical nurse/nursing assistant notes that the rhythm is irregular. Which one of the following assessment activities should be implemented by the practical nurse/nursing assistant immediately?
    1. Assess Mrs. Smith's apical pulse. *— provide more accurate assessment of cardiac rate/rhythm*
    2. Count Mrs. Smith's radial pulse on her other wrist.
    3. Take Mrs. Smith's blood pressure.
    4. Compare the rhythms of Mrs. Smith's apical and radial pulses.

    pulse deficit not rhythm

15. Mrs. Smith becomes confused and responds inappropriately. Which one of the following questions by the practical nurse/nursing assistant best indicates Mrs. Smith's level of orientation? *lost orientation first to time, then place, then person*
    1. "What is your name?"
    2. "What did you eat for breakfast?" *assess memory*
    3. "What do you think about the television program?" *assess interest in environment*
    4. "What does two plus two equal?" *assess logical thought process*

16. Which one of the following entries best meets the obligation for documentation by the practical nurse/nursing assistant caring for Mrs. Smith?
    1. 14 00 h Mrs. Smith appeared restless this afternoon, moaning and pulling at her covers. *name should not be included* *— pain is subjective. Subjective data should be obtained by nurse*
    2. 14 00 h Pulling at covers, moaning. No pain evident.
    3. 14 00 h Pulling at the covers and moaning. States, "I have no pain."
    4. 14 00 h Restless. Mrs. Smith states, "I have no pain." *not objective statement*

17. Mrs. Smith's condition continues to deteriorate throughout the day. Which one of the following interventions by the practical nurse/nursing assistant is the first priority in preparing for an emergency response?
    1. Notify the emergency resuscitation team of Mrs. Smith's deteriorating condition. *notify @ thinks of emergency situation*
    2. Verify the location of the emergency equipment that is used on the unit. *know at all times where it is located and how to use*
    3. Place the emergency resuscitation cart close to Mrs. Smith's bed.
    4. Practice using the emergency equipment with a co-worker.

    kept in designated location available for every client. also place the cart near the client would increase her anxiety

18. Mrs. Smith has become comatose, and her family is at her bedside. Her physician has indicated to the family that Mrs. Smith's death is imminent. Which one of the following statements by the practical nurse/nursing assistant is appropriate in meeting the needs of Mrs. Smith's family? *should support the act of grieving*
    1. "Try not to get upset; you need to support each other." *should be encouraged to take breaks away rather than told to stay*
    2. "Stay at your mother's bedside, as I'm sure she would want you to be there."
    3. "Keep your voices low, because your mother is still able to hear you." *Interact i dyj person as normal as possible*
    4. "You may stay, if you wish, while I care for your mother."

END OF CASE 3

CASE 4

Ken Brown, 17 years old, is admitted to an acute care facility following a diagnosis of depression. Ken's family is very involved with his treatment plan. The practical nurse/nursing assistant is assigned to care for Ken as he begins to stabilize.

QUESTIONS 19 to 23 refer to this case. *normal at rest of an adolescents is 16-18 breaths/min.*

19. The practical nurse/nursing assistant observes that Ken's respirations are 9 breaths/min and shallow with occasional sighs. What term would best describe this type of respiration?
    1. Normal
    2. Bradypnea
    3. Dyspnea
    4. Cheyne-Stokes *irregular, alternating period of apnea and hyperventilation*

20. When gathering data on Ken, which of the following sources is most appropriate for the practical nurse/nursing assistant to use?
    1. Ken's school counselor *breach of confidentiality*
    2. Ken's peers
    3. Ken's parents
    4. Ken's teacher

29

21. Ken tells the practical nurse/nursing assistant, "I can't take it anymore." Which one of the following questions should the practical nurse/nursing assistant ask in assessing Ken's level of safety? *ask direct Q to obtain specific data*

   1. "Do you have any thoughts of harming yourself?"
   2. "What do you know about depression?"
   3. "Have you told your parents that you feel this way?"
   4. "Are you able to look after yourself?"

22. Ken has not eaten in 24 hours. Which one of the following interventions should the practical nurse/nursing assistant implement to encourage him to take nourishment?

   1. Discuss the implications of Ken's behavior with him.
   2. Allow Ken to eat in his room. *socialization assists recovery*
   3. Remove Ken's television privileges until he eats. *a form of punishment, not preferred*
   4. Ask Ken what foods he would prefer to eat.
      respect food preference may ↑ nutritional intake

23. Ken's physician has indicated that it would be beneficial for Ken to begin socializing. Which one of the following interventions by the practical nurse/nursing assistant would be most effective in assisting Ken to socialize?

   1. Arrange a pass for Ken to go home. *could pose safety risk*
   2. Accompany Ken to the patient lounge. *provide opportunity to assess progress and monitor safety*
   3. Provide Ken with two movie passes.
   4. Give Ken a schedule of the social activities on the unit. *he required more than a schedule as he is depressed*

END OF CASE 4

CASE 5

Mrs. Low, 35 years old, underwent an episiotomy when delivering a healthy infant. Following the delivery, the practical nurse/nursing assistant is assigned to care for Mrs. Low. Mrs. Low is found to have heavy lochia and a feeling of lightheadedness.

normal delivery

QUESTIONS 24 to 28 refer to this case.

24. Which of the following manifestations should indicate to the practical nurse/nursing assistant that Mrs. Low is in shock?

   1. Hypertension and pallor
   2. Anxiety and flushed skin
   3. Apprehension and hypertension
   4. Diaphoresis and hypotension

   shock:
   • hypotension
   • pallor
   • diaphoresis

25. Which of the following interventions should the practical nurse/nursing assistant implement first when Mrs. Low faints?
     1. Place Mrs. Low in the supine position and elevate her legs.
     2. Place Mrs. Low in the lateral position and assess for injuries.
     3. Determine the amount of Mrs. Low's lochia and take her vital signs.
     4. Assess Mrs. Low for injuries and take her pulse.

26. When taking Mrs. Low's carotid pulse, which one of the following deviations should the practical nurse/nursing assistant expect?
     1. Rapid, weak pulse
     2. Rapid, full pulse
     3. Slowed, weak pulse
     4. Slowed, full pulse

27. Once Mrs. Low's condition stabilizes, routine postpartum assessment will need to be performed. Which of the following elements are most important to assess in the postpartum period?
     1. Lochial flow and condition of the breasts
     2. Lochial flow and bladder control
     3. Emotional stability and condition of the nipples
     4. Condition of the breasts and bladder control

28. While assessing Mrs. Low's episiotomy, the practical nurse/nursing assistant reinforces perineal care. Which one of the following instructions is most important for the practical nurse/nursing assistant to emphasize?
     1. Use a clean cloth to wash the perineum.
     2. Cleanse from front to back using warm water.
     3. Cleanse from back to front using an antiseptic.
     4. Wipe with clean, dry gauze or tissues.

END OF CASE 5

31

CASE 6

surgical asepsis

Mrs. Long, 45 years old, is scheduled for an abdominal hysterectomy. She is severely obese. The practical nurse/nursing assistant is to provide preoperative and postoperative care.

QUESTIONS 29 to 34 refer to this case.

29. Which one of the following measures is necessary for the practical nurse/nursing assistant to take when performing preoperative care for Mrs. Long?

    to determine what need to be taught by asking direct Qs.

    false reassurance
    1. Reassure Mrs. Long that sexual function will be unaffected by the surgery.
    2. Determine if Mrs. Long knows what to expect postoperatively. *to clarify questions and avoid misunderstanding*
    3. Emphasize the importance of fasting after the evening meal. *preop fasting usu. after midnight*
    4. Physically orient Mrs. Long to the recovery room.
    inappropriate to physically orient her to the room

30. Which one of the following interventions should the practical nurse/nursing assistant implement to encourage Mrs. Long to perform deep breathing and coughing exercises postoperatively?

    should in through nose out through mouth
    1. Tell her to breathe in through her mouth and out through her nose.
    2. Ask Mrs. Long to deep breathe and cough every 4h. *DB/C : q1-2h*
    3. Instruct Mrs. Long to inhale slowly through pursed lips. *inhale through nose, exhale through pursed lips*
    4. Direct Mrs. Long to splint the incision when coughing.
    ↓ discomfort due to forced expiratory most.

31. Which one of the following interventions should the practical nurse/nursing assistant implement when changing Mrs. Long's abdominal dressing?
    sterile glove to maintain surgical asepsis
    1. Apply clean gloves prior to cleansing the incision. *from least contaminated area t prevent introduction of microorg*
    2. Cleanse the incision starting from the most contaminated area.
    3. Use a separate swab for each cleansing stroke. *maintain surgical asepsis*
    4. Wash hands thoroughly prior to removing soiled dressings.
    before beginning procedure, not at this stage

32. Which one of the following interventions should the practical nurse/nursing assistant implement in caring for Mrs. Long's indwelling catheter that has been inserted during surgery?
    urinary meatus cleansed first (from clean to dirty)
    1. Cleanse the catheter prior to cleansing the urinary meatus.
    2. Loop the tubing carefully to allow the urine to drain. *looped tubing: poor drainage, which promote risk of infection*
    3. Use sterile gloves when emptying the closed system. *not necessary*
    4. Keep the drainage bag below the level of the bladder.

33. Which one of the following interventions by the practical nurse/nursing assistant indicates the use of proper body mechanics when positioning Mrs. Long?
    1. Uses smooth and even movements *jerky movt & injuries*
    2. Keeps Mrs. Long's body away from self *weight to be lift : as close as possible*
    3. Adjusts the height of the bed to below waist level *at level of waist to avoid unnecessary bending*
    4. Keeps own upper trunk flexed *upper trunk should be erect*

34. Which one of the following interventions should the practical nurse/nursing assistant implement when initially standing Mrs. Long on the evening of her surgery?
    1. Check the time of anesthetic administration. *need to know last time c analgesic was given*
    2. Request assistance from another health care team member. *obese, too heavy for one person*
    3. Use a mechanical lift to get Mrs. Long into a standing position. *not promote postop ambulat?*
    4. Attach the urinary drainage bag to Mrs. Long's gown. *unnecessary : she is not leaving the bedside*

END OF CASE 6

CASE 7

venous

Jack Harris, 68 years old, is admitted to hospital with a chronic, nonhealing ulcer on his ankle. For many years, he has suffered from peripheral vascular disease related to venous insufficiency. The ulcer is being treated with I.V. antibiotics and topical medications. Mr. Harris shows signs of inadequate nutrition and poor hygiene.

QUESTIONS 35 to 40 refer to this case.

35. The practical nurse/nursing assistant encourages Mr. Harris to include fresh fruit and vegetables in his diet whenever possible. What is the most important reason for making this recommendation to Mr. Harris? *promote healing*
    1. Fresh fruits and vegetables contain vitamin C.
    2. High-fiber diets promote regular elimination in the elderly. *problem is poor healing, not constipat?*
    3. Raw fruits and vegetables are more easily digested. *digest more slowly as they contain large amount of cellulose*
    4. Fresh fruits and vegetables require less preparation.

36. When affirming consent for Mr. Harris's foot care, which one of the following procedures is most appropriate for the practical nurse/nursing assistant to follow?

    1. Ask Mr. Harris if he will permit the practical nurse/nursing assistant to do his foot care. *important to verify consent for care*
    2. Have Mr. Harris sign a consent form. *for obtaining consent, not affirming consent, usu. reserved for invasive procedure*
    3. Have a second health care team member witness Mr. Harris's verbal consent. *witness not necessary*
    4. Consult with Mr. Harris's family regarding his foot care. *if pt competent, no need to consult family*

37. Mr. Harris asks the practical nurse/nursing assistant why he is receiving antibiotics through the I.V. and not in some other form. Which one of the following responses is most appropriate for the practical nurse/nursing assistant to make?

    1. "Oral antibiotics may upset your stomach."
    2. "It is more economical to give antibiotics in I.V. form." *not true*
    3. "Antibiotics in I.V. form build up a useful level in the blood stream."
    4. "That is a good question. You should ask your physician during the next visit." *not address client's Qs*

38. Which one of the following observations should indicate to the practical nurse/nursing assistant that Mr. Harris needs special foot care?

    1. Drying of the skin *normal, skin emollients*
    2. Lowering of the arch *not necessarily cause problems or require special care*
    3. Loss of subcutaneous tissue *shoes may be too loose c loss of sc, not a problem until redness is noted*
    4. Hard, thickened nails *result fm: inadequate nutrition, poor circulation*

39. Which one of the following interventions should the practical nurse/nursing assistant implement when administering a topical medicated cream to Mr. Harris's open leg ulcer?

    1. Use a sterile applicator to apply the cream. *open wound: sterile*
    2. Use a clean glove to apply the cream.
    3. Apply the cream evenly with clean fingertips.
    4. Instruct Mr. Harris to spread the cream with his fingers.

40. Which of the following initial steps should the practical nurse/nursing assistant take to encourage Mr. Harris to take responsibility for his own health care? *determine readiness to learn and present level of understanding, also an open-ended*

    1. Ask Mr. Harris what he thinks is the reason for his leg ulcer not healing.
    2. Indicate to Mr. Harris that he is capable of learning to change his own dressing.
    3. Question Mr. Harris to determine if he realizes that he is malnourished. *not determine readiness to l*
    4. Discuss with Mr. Harris the side effects of the medications he is taking. *not as first step*

END OF CASE 7

34

INDEPENDENT QUESTIONS

QUESTIONS 41 to 103 do not refer to a case.

41. Mrs. Young is obese and requires the use of a mechanical lifting device. Which one of the following practices must the practical nurse/nursing assistant follow during the procedure?
    1. Ask another health care team member for assistance. *Two persons are always required to be present if mechanical lifting is used*
    2. Apply the brakes during the transfer. *the machine cannot be moved within room*
    3. Keep the base of support narrow for easier maneuvering.
    4. Check the equipment following the lift.

42. Ms. Colleen O'Brien, 72 years old, is dyspneic. Which one of the following positions would most likely help Ms. O'Brien to breathe easier?
    1. High-Fowler's *provides max. lung expansion*
    2. Low-Fowler's
    3. Supine *abd. push upward on diaphragm decreasing intrathoracic space for lung expansion*
    4. Right lateral

43. Andy Stuart, 70 years old, has Alzheimer disease. He is becoming increasingly confused at mealtime and, as a result, he often does not eat. Which one of the following interventions implemented by the practical nurse/nursing assistant would best assist Andy in maintaining his nutritional intake? *confused: may not remember how to use utensils ↑ self feeding*
    1. Provide Andy with finger foods.
    2. Assist Andy by demonstrating how to feed himself. *Demonstration not comprehended by Alzheimer disease*
    3. Present Andy with a new and interesting food at each meal.
    4. Offer Andy a number of foods to choose from at meals. *Alzheimer: not tolerate new food well, more likely to eat familiar food*

Many food choice increase confusion and frustration in Alzheimer patient. Better to reduce no. of choice

44. Mrs. Grace Andrews, 68 years old, has had major abdominal surgery. Mrs. Andrews consistently wears her antiembolic stockings and does her leg exercises as requested, but is presently experiencing pain in her left calf. Which one of the following interventions should be implemented by the practical nurse/nursing assistant in response to this finding? *stop calf pain is often a manifestation of thrombosis*
    1. Encourage Mrs. Andrews to exercise less frequently.
    2. Report Mrs. Andrews' leg pain to the nurse-in-charge immediately.
    3. Remove Mrs. Andrews' antiembolic stockings. *may threatened safety if she's thrombosis*
    4. Continue to monitor Mrs. Andrews' pain throughout the day.

Pain should be reported as it may signify a thrombosis

45. Which one of the following qualities best describes normal, adult feces?
    1. Narrow, pencil-shaped *obstruction or rapid peristalsis*
    2. Mucous coated *indicate irritation, not normal*
    3. Characteristic odor *result of food digested, normal*
    4. Black and tarry *indicate iron ingestion or upper gastrointestinal bleeding*

35

GO TO NEXT PAGE

46. A practical nurse/nursing assistant, who just came on shift, finds the assigned client sitting on the floor. The side rails on the bed are up. Which one of the following statements on the incident report is the best record of the practical nurse's/nursing assistant's findings?

indicate objective data observed

1. "Side rails placed up by night shift and client fell while climbing over them."
2. "Client found in sitting position on the floor beside the bed, side rails up." *judgmental*
3. "Side rails put up in error, client found in sitting position on the floor."
4. "Client found on floor after having climbed over the side rails." *personal assumption*

47. Jim Jones, a 68-year-old teacher, normally wears a hearing aid, but has forgotten it at home. The practical nurse/nursing assistant is providing Jim with preoperative instructions. Which one of the following communication techniques will best help Jim understand what is being said?

cause more distortion than ↑ their volume

1. Speak into his least affected ear much louder than usual.
2. Speak slowly using a higher pitch. *harder to understand lower pitch is recommended*
3. Clearly mouth the instructions. *may not read lips well — no guarantee fully understand instructions*
4. Write the instructions on paper. *ensure receipt of necess. information*

48. Which of the following assessment data on a 90-year-old female client would be important for the practical nurse/nursing assistant to report?

1. Spotty pigmentation in areas exposed to the sun *normal age related changes*
2. Thinning, graying hair
3. Improperly fitting dentures *could interfere c ability to eat, and cause mouth sores*
4. Folding, sagging skin

49. Mrs. Moore, 69 years old, is scheduled for an incisional hernia repair tomorrow. She states to the practical nurse/nursing assistant caring for her, "I'm really scared about my surgery tomorrow." Which one of the following responses by the practical nurse/nursing assistant best demonstrates concern for Mrs. Moore?

belittle her anxiety, not demonstrate concern

1. "This surgery is minor, but even minor surgery can be very frightening."
2. "It is frightening. I recently had surgery myself and was very frightened." *inappropriate shift focus LPN experience*
3. "The thought of surgery is frightening. How can I help you?" *acknowledge feeling, open routes for communication*
4. "You've had surgery before, so what is your concern about this surgery?"

Reminding does not address to feelings. Feelings need to be recognized.

50. The practical nurse/nursing assistant is answering a call light and discovers that Karen, 14 years old, has just vomited. There is a large amount of gastric contents mixed with bloody streaks on Karen's gown and on the floor. After notifying the nurse-in-charge, which one of the following interventions should the practical nurse/nursing assistant implement next? *specimen not necessary*

1. Collect a specimen of the emesis for the nurse-in-charge to assess.
2. Gown and glove before providing care to Karen. *universal precautions*
3. Call housekeeping to clean the floor after providing care to Karen. *safety hazard*
4. Gown, glove, and mask before providing care to Karen.

low risk of splashing mask not necessary

36

A9-9996

51. A 75-year-old female client, diagnosed with hematuria, has pulled out her indwelling catheter. Which one of the following interventions is most important for the practical nurse/nursing assistant to implement? *wearing glove during care more important*

    1. Wash hands thoroughly following catheter disposal. *unless contamination of outside of bag*
    2. Double bag the catheter in preparation for disposal.
    (3.) Wear disposable gloves to care for the client's catheter. *protect caregiver, maintain universal precautions*
    4. Use a gown and gloves to administer care. *gown not necessary if no splashing*

52. Cory, a practical nurse/nursing assistant, was asked by the nurse-in-charge to give an enema to Mrs. Sands. After administering the enema, Cory discovers that the physician's order was for an enema to be given to Mrs. Talbot, and that Mrs. Sands was to receive a suppository. After reporting the mistake to the nurse-in-charge, which one of the following actions must the practical nurse/nursing assistant take?

    1. Record that incorrect directions from the nurse-in-charge were the cause of the error. *failure of LPN to verify Dr's order prior to adm. of enema*
    2. Administer an enema to Mrs. Talbot so that both clients will have the required bowel evacuation. *wrong to assume mrs. Sands had appropriate bowel evacuation*
    3. Inform Mrs. Sands that it is not necessary to have a suppository because an enema has the same effect. *Sands had the right to know error, but nurse in charge need to be consulted first*
    (4.) Document the circumstances and sequence of events that led to the error. *Provide info for review of error so facility can take actions for quality assurance and risk management*

53. A 70-year-old female client asks the practical nurse/nursing assistant to help her care for her long, curly hair. Which one of the following actions should the practical nurse/nursing assistant take when caring for this client's hair? *Sebaceous gland function diminishes c̄ age*

    1. Brush her hair until it begins to shine.
    2. Comb the hair with a fine-toothed comb. *Not suitable for curly hair*
    (3.) Use a wide-toothed comb to remove tangles.
    4. Put her hair in a hairnet. *likely ↑ tangles in long hair.*

54. Mrs. Carter, 72 years old, lives alone. During the interview, which one of the following assessment findings is the most important for the practical nurse/nursing assistant to include in Mrs. Carter's care plan? *report most important piece of information*

    1. She has her grandson help her with the yardwork.
    2. She takes the bus to and from the grocery store.
    (3.) She uses a raised toilet seat in the bathroom. *indicate decreased function → safety issue*
    4. She usually wears slacks and sweaters around the house.

55. Which one of the following interventions should the practical nurse/nursing assistant implement to provide Mrs. Rosa, 75 years old, with denture care?

    1. Use a clean hand to remove both dentures. *need disposable glove*
    2. Rinse the dentures in hot water. *easily damaged by bending or twisting*
    (3.) Brush the dentures over a water-filled emesis basin. *to ↓ breakage if dropped, should be held over water c̄ brushing*
    4. Soak the dentures in mouthwash. *not clean the denture properly*

GO TO NEXT PAGE

56. While the practical nurse/nursing assistant is preparing a client for his physiotherapy appointment, the meal trays arrive. A client in the next bed asks for his pain medication, and another client returns from the recovery room. Which of the following client situations should be the practical nurse's/nursing assistant's priority?

prioritize:
· level of risk
· unknown factors
· routine care
· scheduled appointments

1. Client returning from recovery room
2. Client in pain
3. Client with physiotherapy appointment
4. Clients' meal trays

57. Greg, 26 years old, is hospitalized in traction. In an attempt to use the bedpan independently, Greg has soiled himself and his linens. Which one of the following statements by the practical nurse/nursing assistant is most likely to support Greg?

1. "Don't be embarrassed about it, Greg. This is my job, and it's no problem." *invalidate his feeling*
2. "I'll bring you a regular bedpan because this slipper pan just isn't deep enough." *make him feel more dependent*
3. "I'll bet it's been a long time since this happened. I promise not to tell anyone."
4. "It can be difficult to try to do things independently and experience an unplanned result." *indicate care of feeling → ↓ isolation, enhance support*

58. Mr. Moreno, 47 years old, has multiple sclerosis. Upon washing his back, the practical nurse/nursing assistant notices some changes to the skin on his coccyx area. Which one of the following changes indicates the first stage of a pressure sore?

1. Increasing loss of sensation to the coccyx region *predisposition of pressure sore, but not the first stage*
2. A reddened area over the coccyx region
3. A darkened cyanotic area over the coccyx region *stage two in pressure sore*
4. Increasing dependent edema to the coccyx region *edema: predisposing factor to pressure sore.*

59. Tammy, 4 years old, has just returned to the pediatric unit following a tonsillectomy when she vomits some dark red blood. After placing Tammy on her side, which of the following interventions should the practical nurse/nursing assistant implement next?

postop vomiting & evidence of dark red blood doesn't need to be reported stat.

1. Leave Tammy momentarily and inform the nurse-in-charge of her condition.
2. Put on the call light, and inform the nurse-in-charge of Tammy's condition.
3. Take Tammy's vital signs, and report and record the findings.
4. Suction Tammy's throat, and report and record the findings. *not recommended for pt who had a tonsillectomy as it can disrupt the surgical site*

60. Mrs. George, a frail 85-year-old who is usually able to transfer via a one-person assist, tells the practical nurse/nursing assistant that she feels weak. Which one of the following transfer methods is most appropriate for the practical nurse/nursing assistant to use?

1. A one-person standing transfer *unsafe if weak*
2. A two-person lift
3. A mechanical lift *∵ pt can bear weight*
4. A two-person standing transfer

1.16

61. Mark Hanoi, a pleasant 24-year-old, is being monitored following a minor head injury sustained in a hockey game. His neurological vital signs have been within normal limits. Which of the following behaviors should alert the practical nurse/nursing assistant that his condition might be deteriorating?

1. He states that he will never play hockey again.
2. He awakens from sleep calling out the name of a friend. *not indicate ↓LOC*
3. He yells at the practical nurse/nursing assistant to leave him alone. *irritability: symptoms of ↓LOC*
4. He says he feels fine and asks to be discharged.

62. Sandy, 3 years old, is recovering from surgery on the unit and is on a clear, fluid diet. Which one of the following meals is most appropriate for her?

full fluid
1. Apple juice and gelatin
2. Milkshake and popsicle
3. Ice cream and gelatin
4. Tea and broth → *clear fluid*
not appropriate for 3 yr old child

63. Mr. Rose, 48 years old, is experiencing a respiratory arrest. Where would the practical nurse/nursing assistant most likely find the emergency resuscitation equipment?

1. In the oxygen storage room
2. On the unit's crash cart
3. In the medication room
4. In the intensive care unit or emergency department *emergency equipment kept on each unit.*

64. A 20-year-old female client diagnosed with anorexia nervosa develops redness of the coccyx area. Which one of the following interventions should the practical nurse/nursing assistant implement? *↑ ischemia*

1. Provide the client with a foam ring to sit on.
2. Have the client sleep on her side. *↑ pressure while on hips*
3. Encourage the client to change her position every 1–2 hours. *relieve pressure around superficial capillary allow for compensation & for temporary ischemia*
4. Suggest the client take a warm tub bath. *heat, ↑ pressure.*

65. Which one of the following actions taken by the practical nurse/nursing assistant best promotes client safety? *for protection of carer rather than pt*

1. Attend an inservice education session on dealing with client aggression.
2. Maintain an optimal level of physical fitness. *protection of a caregiver*
3. Complete the necessary incident reports within 24 hours. *protection of agency/staff*
4. Check topical medications three times prior to administration. *to ↓ administration error, and is a safety issue for patient*

GO TO NEXT PAGE
A9-9996

66. Mr. Rask, 89 years old, is having his blood pressure assessed by the practical nurse/nursing assistant. The practical nurse/nursing assistant is unsure of the point at which the sound of the systolic pressure was first heard. Which of the following actions by the practical nurse/nursing assistant are appropriate in this situation?
   1. Reinflate the cuff and repeat the reading immediately.
   2. Ask a team member to verify the reading.
   3. Reapply the cuff and take the reading again.
   4. Reinflate the cuff 30 seconds later and repeat the reading.

67. Jane Songster, 38 years old, has just had surgery for breast cancer. She states, "I can't believe that this has happened to me." Which one of the following initial responses by the practical nurse/nursing assistant would likely be most therapeutic?
   1. "I will be available whenever you want to talk about this; just let me know."
   2. "I can call someone from the breast cancer support group to come and talk to you, if you would like."
   3. "Why don't you believe that this has happened to you?"
   4. "May I sit with you awhile?"

68. Eighteen-month-old Sarah has an upper respiratory infection. The practical nurse/nursing assistant determines that Sarah's respirations are 30 breaths/min and regular, and that she has a loose cough. Which one of the following interventions is most appropriate for the practical nurse/nursing assistant to implement?
   1. Record these data on Sarah's chart.
   2. Advise Sarah's physician.
   3. Have another member of the health care team assess Sarah's respiratory status.
   4. Return and reassess Sarah's respiratory status in 1 hour.

69. Mr. Beisner, 65 years old, has had hip replacement surgery. Which one of the following pieces of information is most important for the practical nurse/nursing assistant to consider when assessing his postoperative pain?
   1. Mr. Beisner's ranking of his current level of pain
   2. Mr. Beisner's past experiences with pain
   3. Methods Mr. Beisner has used in the past to control pain
   4. Cultural factors that may influence Mr. Beisner's perception of pain

70. Miss Young has a history of I.V. drug abuse. The physician has asked her permission to administer an HIV test. Which one of the following questions should the practical nurse/nursing assistant ask first when assessing Miss Young?
   1. "Are you aware of the current treatment for AIDS?"
   2. "Are you sexually active?"
   3. "Would you like me to call your family?"
   4. "Do you understand the purpose of this test?"

40

A9-9996

71. Mrs. Vitas, a 70-year-old palliative care client, wishes to die at home. Her family wants her to stay in the palliative care unit. Which one of the following responses should the practical nurse/nursing assistant make to Mrs. Vitas and her family to help them try to deal with this situation?

    1. "Have you had the opportunity to discuss this among yourselves?"
    2. "Would information about community palliative care services be helpful?" *pass responsibility too early*
    3. "Could a member of the pastoral care team help you sort out this dilemma?"
    4. "Would you like me to stay to offer an objective point of view?" *Judgmental*

PN viewpoint may not be objective

72. In the 2 days since her admission, Giselle John, 18 years old, has directed several abusive outbursts toward staff. Which one of the following actions indicates the practical nurse/nursing assistant is in the planning phase of developing a nursing care plan for Giselle?

    1. Recording a successful approach used with Giselle
    2. Reporting several of Giselle's comments during her outbursts *Assessment*
    3. Trying several different approaches when doing Giselle's care *Implementation*
    4. Identifying possible sources of Giselle's abusive behavior *Assessment*

73. A 60-year-old female client is suffering from congestive heart failure. Which one of the following interventions should the practical nurse/nursing assistant implement when measuring her abdominal girth? *provide a consistent, accurate measure*

    1. Take the measurement at the level of the client's umbilicus.
    2. Compare the client's chest and abdominal circumferences.
    3. Place the client on her back with her knees flexed. *Place on back could aggravate CHF*
    4. Instruct the client to inhale deeply prior to taking the measurement.

should relax and breath normally to avoid distortion of measurement

74. Tony, 3 years old, has been toilet trained, but has regressed to wetting the bed while in the hospital. His parents want him to wear a diaper only at night. Which one of the following entries by the practical nurse/nursing assistant best communicates this information to the health care team?

    1. Diaper h.s.
    2. Diaper p.r.n.
    3. Diaper q.s. — *as much as may be needed*
    4. Diaper q.d.

75. Jennifer, 4 years old, has been accompanied by her mother and is being prepared by the practical nurse/nursing assistant for a physical examination. Which one of the following interventions should the practical nurse/nursing assistant implement after getting her partially undressed?

inappropriate to ask mum leave

    1. Send Jennifer's mother out of the room while attempting to collect a urine specimen.

concept of time is not fully understood by a 4 yr old

    2. Reassure Jennifer that the physician will be in to see her in about 15 minutes.

imaginative and like to pretend

    3. Allow Jennifer to listen to her doll's heart through a stethoscope.

    4. Remind Jennifer to sit quietly and refrain from touching any equipment.

sitting quietly & appropriate distractions is difficult for a 4-yr old

76. Kelly, 12 years old, has had major abdominal surgery. In caring for Kelly, which one of the following situations requires the use of medical asepsis by the practical nurse/nursing assistant?

medical vs surgical asepsis

    1. Care of surgical wounds

    2. Maintenance of nasogastric tubes

    3. Insertion of an indwelling urinary catheter

    4. Removal of sutures

surgical asepsis

77. The practical nurse/nursing assistant is told by a nurse that Tony, 18 months old, is to have elbow restraints used on the physician's order. Which one of the following steps should the practical nurse/nursing assistant take first?

    1. Check Tony's chart for the order. *1st step in carrying out procedure*

    2. Explain to Tony's parent what is to be done. *done following verificat² of an order*

    3. Obtain well-padded restraints. *after the order verificat² of order*

    4. Consider alternative approaches to restraining Tony.

before the order

78. An 80-year-old male client is receiving meals at home from a volunteer agency. While visiting an outpatient clinic, he tells the practical nurse/nursing assistant that he is not able to eat the food. Which one of the following factors is most important to consider when recording this client's food intake?

    1. The client's economic status

    2. The client's personal preferences — *one major factor to determine what he eats*

    3. The client's social status

    4. The client's environment *influence storage/preparation rather than food intake*

79. Mr. Levin, 23 years old, has just been admitted to the hospital after a motor vehicle accident in which he sustained internal injuries. He is alert, oriented, and experiencing abdominal pain. Which of the following manifestations should indicate to the practical nurse/nursing assistant that Mr. Levin is bleeding internally? *to oxygenate o less circulating blood*

    1. A drop in blood pressure and increased pulse rate

    2. A drop in pulse rate and increased respiratory rate

    3. An elevated blood pressure and slowed respiratory rate

    4. A stable blood pressure and bounding pulse *pulse rapid and trying to compensate for diminished blood volume*

A9-9996

↑ R.
BP stable or slightly ↑ initially but subtle to detect

80. The practical nurse/nursing assistant is assigned to maintain an intake and output record for Jane, 34 years old. Which one of the following measures by the practical nurse/nursing assistant is most appropriate in maintaining this record?
    1. Ensure Jane uses a commode for voiding. *urine collection device can be placed in toilet*
    2. Teach Jane to assist in recording her intake and output. *help should be enlisted*
    3. Keep track of Jane's fluid balance on a notepad in the practical nurse's/nursing assistant's pocket. *placed @ bedside to assist documentation*
    4. Remove the water pitcher from Jane's room. *no need to remove, but water consumed needs to be recorded*

81. Which one of the following charting examples is correct when the practical nurse/nursing assistant records client care? *Chart each time ∆*
    1. Dressing changed frequently using sterile technique *no amount/type of drainage*
    2. Drainage noted and reported to unit manager immediately
    3. Abdominal dressing changed for scant, serous discharge *location, amount and type of drainage*
    4. Routine dressing change performed during shift *∅ location nor amount/type of drainage*

82. Bill Brown, an 85-year-old client who is overweight and arthritic, is on a bedpan in bed. Which one of the following approaches should the practical nurse/nursing assistant take to remove Mr. Brown's bedpan?
    1. Explain to Mr. Brown how to remove the bedpan himself. *difficult for him; physical limitation*
    2. Roll Mr. Brown onto his side. *safer/easier to roll to side ∵ obese, physical limitation*
    3. Ask Mr. Brown to raise his buttocks by flexing his knees. *overweight + elderly · unlikely to lift buttock*
    4. Have Mr. Brown grasp the overhead trapeze to lift his buttocks. *overweight: unlikely to support his weight č his arms*

83. On assessing 11-year-old Lois's I.V. site, the practical nurse/nursing assistant observes redness along the path of the vein. Which one of the following terms best refers to this complication?
    1. Phlebitis *→ more accurate description*
    2. Infiltration *→ swelling/pallor*
    3. Bacteremia *→ systemic nature: nausea, chills, malaise*
    4. Inflammation *→ general term*

84. The practical nurse/nursing assistant is caring for Mrs. Harper, 44 years old, who is dying of breast cancer. Mrs. Harper has a supportive husband and 3 children. Her 10-year-old daughter asks the practical nurse/nursing assistant if her mother is going to die today. Which one of the following responses by the practical nurse/nursing assistant is most appropriate to give to Mrs. Harper's daughter?
    1. "What has your father told you about how your mother is doing? Has someone said that she is going to die?" *avoiding the issue*
    2. "Why don't you go back into your mother's room and tell her about school. We can talk about this with your father later." *putting her off ↑ sense of distress*
    3. "Your mother is very sick but I don't know if she will die today. Let's sit down and talk about what you're feeling." *truthful, offer no false hope, be available to listen to concerns*
    4. "Your mother might die today but nobody knows when we will die. Can I call someone for you to talk with?" *suggesting sb else causes feeling of angry and rejected as child indicates comfort to talk to pn.*

85. Todd, 2 years old, is to go to the playroom in his regular clothes. Which of the following actions by the practical nurse/nursing assistant would best assist Todd to dress?
    1. Allow Todd to dress completely by himself. *still need some help c̄ fasteners*
    2. Provide privacy, and then dress Todd completely.
    3. Encourage independent dressing by letting Todd do what he can. *encourage independ dress to foster auton*
    4. Dress Todd, allowing him to choose his clothes. *should dress relatively independently*

86. Terry, a practical nurse/nursing assistant, overhears a co-worker make a sexual remark to an adult client. This is the second time that Terry has heard a similar remark from the co-worker. When approached by Terry, the co-worker insists that the remark was made as a joke and that the client had also made a sexual remark in return. Which one of the following actions is most appropriate for the practical nurse/nursing assistant to take first regarding the incident?
    1. Assume that appropriate measures have been taken as the co-worker has been approached.
    2. Consider the incident as a mutually acceptable verbal exchange between two adults. *safeguard client maintain professional conduct c̄ ∅ assumption it is okay*
    3. Discuss the incident with the client before taking any further action. *collect additio info. not resolve the issue*
    4. Report the incident to the nurse-in-charge. *ethical issues not resolved as right/wrong. action to resolve the issue*

87. The practical nurse/nursing assistant is feeding Mr. Brown, a 74-year-old client who recently had a cerebrovascular accident. Mr. Brown begins to cough and has difficulty breathing. Which one of the following measures should the practical nurse/nursing assistant implement immediately? *okay if cannot breath, speak, or cough*
    1. Perform abdominal thrusts to dislodge the food.
    2. Commence suctioning to remove the obstruction. *too deep to be suctioned, also likely to △ to a complete blockage*
    3. Encourage the client to cough out the food.
    4. Call an emergency code to get help with the situation. *not necessitate an emergency code at this time.*

88. The physician has ordered a heat lamp treatment for Mr. Hall, a 26-year-old male client. What is the primary reason for the practical nurse/nursing assistant to consult the procedure manual prior to implementation of this technique? *established practice to follow*
    1. The agency's accepted procedure will be stated in the manual.
    2. A safe method of administering this treatment in all situations will be outlined. *q. that to asses*
    3. Equipment-related errors will be avoided if the procedure is reviewed. *misuse, misfunct still poss*
    4. Sufficient instructions for operation of equipment will be provided. *may not provide sufficient instructions professional responsibility to seek verification if unfamiliar c̄ procedure.*

44

1.22

89. Mr. Griffin, 85 years old, is waiting for placement in a long-term care facility. Mr. Griffin asks the practical nurse/nursing assistant, "What if my wife forgets to take her medication or has a fall when I am not at home?" Which one of the following questions should the practical nurse/nursing assistant ask?

1. "Does your wife's medication affect her balance?" *recognition of client concern*
2. "How often has your wife fallen in the past?"
3. "Do you feel concerned about your wife's safety if you're not with her?" *listening & reflecting the meaning*
4. "Have you made any arrangements for your wife's care when you're not there?"
make assumption that client has never expressed

90. Mr. Ralph Schneider, 74 years old, has been admitted to hospital for assessment of a possible arterial occlusion of his right lower leg. Which of the following findings concerning Mr. Schneider's foot would most likely indicate a loss of arterial circulation?

1. Cyanotic and cold to the touch *venous congestion arterial sufficient*
2. Edematous and warm to the touch
3. Dark red and cool to the touch *venous congestion arterial insufficient*
4. Dry and hot to the touch
dry not indicate a specific circulatory difficulty

91. Mandy, 3 years old, is toilet trained but has recently had several episodes of wetting her underpants, for which medical reasons have been ruled out. Which one of the following suggestions by the practical nurse/nursing assistant should assist Mandy's parents in reestablishing her elimination routine?

1. Take Mandy to the toilet at regular intervals throughout the day.
2. Restrict Mandy's fluid intake. *not contribute to bladder control*
3. Have Mandy wear training pants. *diminish self esteem*
4. Withdraw a privilege each time Mandy wets her underpants. *inappropriate*

92. A cardiac arrest code has been called and resuscitation is under way. Which one of the following interventions by the practical nurse/nursing assistant is most appropriate during the resuscitation?

1. Check that oxygen and suction equipment are available. *already in use*
2. Move any laundry hampers or wheelchairs out of the hallways. *important before the team arrives*
3. Offer to transport blood specimens to the laboratory. *inappropriate to leave the unit in an emergency*
4. Provide essential care to the remaining clients on the unit.
take over the care of other clients in an emergency

93. Mrs. White has been told by her physician that her newborn has a club foot. She asks the practical nurse/nursing assistant what this means. How should the practical nurse/nursing assistant respond to Mrs. White's question?

1. Indicate to Mrs. White that a discussion of this nature is outside the practical nurse's/nursing assistant's responsibilities. *within the role to reinforce explanation*
2. Provide Mrs. White with the name of a pediatric orthopedic surgeon. *unethical*
3. Determine Mrs. White's understanding and clarify as necessary.
4. Explain the term "club foot" to Mrs. White and its possible complications.
1st assess client's level of understanding

Clubfoot: congenital deformity deviation of metatarsal bones of forefoot. Tx: splints and casts or surgery

94. Mr. Eberle, 80 years old, is becoming more anorexic as his functional abilities decrease. What is the best approach for the practical nurse/nursing assistant to take to address Mr. Eberle's nutritional deficit?

    1. Recommend eggnogs and milkshakes. *may not be preferred food*
    2. Offer him food supplements. *improve nutritional status*
    3. Promote eating small portions. *not address to key concern of nutritional deficit*
    4. Encourage the ingestion of high energy foods.
    not all high energy foods are nutritionally sound

95. Which of the following interventions are most appropriate for the practical nurse/nursing assistant to implement when bathing 3-year-old Jake?

    1. Allow Jake to help the practical nurse/nursing assistant wash his face and hands. *should not be limited to face/hands*
    2. Let Jake play in the tub and check on him frequently. *risk of drowning*
    3. Help Jake run water for his tub bath. *potential for injury fm burn*
    4. Supervise Jake with bathing and encourage his assistance. *maintain safety* *promote autonomy and independence*

96. Kathy St. John, a 23-year-old client with asthma, has been admitted with a respiratory infection. She has a frequent cough that is producing thick sputum. Which one of the following actions should the practical nurse/nursing assistant take to best ensure medical asepsis? *to deal c secretions*

    1. Wear gloves followed by good handwashing when handling soiled tissues.
    2. Double bag the soiled tissues before discarding them in the utility room.
    3. Provide Kathy with an adequate supply of tissues and garbage bags.
    4. Change the garbage bag at Kathy's bedside every 8 hours.
    likely more often than q8h c frequent cough + sputum

97. Wade, 18 years old, has been admitted with a diagnosis that includes "possible HIV." Sally, his girlfriend, is a close friend of the practical nurse/nursing assistant assigned to Wade's care. Blood tests to screen for HIV have been ordered. Sally has asked the practical nurse/nursing assistant if Wade has AIDS. Which one of the following actions by the practical nurse/nursing assistant would be most appropriate?

    1. Refer Sally to Wade's physician. *confidentiality*
    2. Inform Sally that the test results are not back.
    3. Tell Sally that she should have an HIV test. *implies +ve result*
    4. Suggest that Sally talk directly to Wade.
    consider ethics/legalities/personal relationships
    client is the only person who can discuss this info c other person.

98. Rebecca, 12 years old, has limited mobility following a motor vehicle accident. Which one of the following approaches should the practical nurse/nursing assistant take when providing her with hygienic care? *inappropriate s knowing needs/preferences*

    1. Offer to take Rebecca to the shower in a shower-chair.
    2. Assist Rebecca to the sink to bathe. *may not address her needs/preferences*
    3. Provide Rebecca with the necessary supplies to wash herself. *may require more assistance*
    4. Ask Rebecca how much help she would like with bathing.
    consider personal preferences of client

A9-9996

99. The practical nurse/nursing assistant is distributing special diet trays to clients on the unit. John Smith, 18 years old, has no identification bracelet. Which one of the following measures should the practical nurse/nursing assistant take to ensure verification of this client's identity with the special diet tray label?
    1. Call John by his full name and ensure he responds to his name. *may still respond if call the wrong name*
    2. Ask John to say his full name.
    3. Ensure that the room and bed number match the diet card on the tray. *may be in different room*
    4. Seek the assistance of another client in identifying John. *not accurate way to verify client's name*

100. Which one of the following cleansing sequences should the practical nurse/nursing assistant use to maintain the principles of medical asepsis when providing perineal care for an adult male client?
    1. Groin, scrotum, penile shaft, glans penis
    2. Penile shaft, glans penis, groin, scrotum
    3. Glans penis, penile shaft, scrotum, groin *away from urethral meatus*
    4. Scrotum, penile shaft, glans penis, groin

101. Mrs. Hrabar, 72 years old, has suffered a right-sided cerebrovascular accident with hemiparesis of her left arm and leg. Which one of the following measures by the practical nurse/nursing assistant allows Mrs. Hrabar to have accessibility to her call system?
    1. Place the call bell on the bed near Mrs. Hrabar's dominant hand. *client may be left handed*
    2. Put the call bell on the left side of Mrs. Hrabar's pillow. *not appropriate on left side*
    3. Attach the call bell to the side rail within Mrs. Hrabar's visual field. *no guarantee client can reach*
    4. Ensure the call bell is within Mrs. Hrabar's reach on the right side of her bed.

102. Penny, 4 years old, is hospitalized with a diagnosis of insulin dependent (Type I) diabetes mellitus. Which one of the following statements by Penny should the practical nurse/nursing assistant report immediately?
    1. "My foot hurts." *foot injury. not necessary to report immediately*
    2. "I feel funny inside." *symptoms of hypoglycemia*
    3. "I saw a monster in the closet." *preschooler's may have fear / imaginary monster*
    4. "I hate my Mom." *not unusual if child views hospitalization is due to parents responsibility*

103. Mr. Leskyf is admitted to the local psychiatric facility. While in the cafeteria, his wife overhears two health care workers discussing his condition. Which one of the following terms most accurately describes this situation?
    1. Libel *written statement that conveys unfavorable impression*
    2. Breach of ethics *of moral behavior*
    3. Breach of confidentiality *violate right of privacy*
    4. Verbal assault *mean to hurt the client*

71/103

END OF INDEPENDENT QUESTIONS

END OF BOOK 1

A9-9996

CANADIAN NURSES ASSOCIATION

TESTING DIVISION

PRACTICAL NURSE/NURSING ASSISTANT
REGISTRATION/LICENSURE EXAMINATION

CANDIDATE NUMBER

SIGNATURE

BOOK 2

TEST FORM 9997

READ THE INSTRUCTIONS AND SAMPLE QUESTIONS INSIDE THE FRONT COVER

CANADIAN NURSES ASSOCIATION
ASSOCIATION DES INFIRMIÈRES ET INFIRMIERS DU CANADA

INSTRUCTIONS

A) TESTING TIME AND MATERIAL

You will have two hours and 15 minutes to work on this test book. The starting and finishing times will be announced and you will be advised when there are 30 and 15 minutes working time remaining. If at any time you have any questions about what you should do, raise your hand and an invigilator will assist you.

You will be advised whether you may leave the examination room if you finish the test book before the time is up. You must **stop** working when the signal is given. An invigilator will check your test book and answer sheet **before** you leave.

Clear your desk of all materials except your identification card, answer sheet, test book, pencils, and eraser. **Do not** fold, bend, or tear your answer sheet, as this could affect the scoring of your test.

B) ANSWER SHEET

Write your name, date of birth, date of writing, and test title in the corresponding boxes. Enter in your CANDIDATE NUMBER, the WRITING CENTRE CODE, and the TEST FORM and fill in the corresponding ovals. If you do not have a candidate number leave this section blank. Complete the box labeled LANGUAGE OF WRITING.

Be sure the mark you make for each answer is black, fills the oval, and contains the number corresponding to the number of the answer you have chosen. Do **not** fill in more than one oval for a question or you will not get credit for it. Erase **completely** any answer you wish to change and mark your new choice in the correct oval. An incomplete erasure may be read incorrectly as an intended answer. Do not press too heavily on your pencil or you may damage the answer sheet.

Note that the questions on the answer sheet are numbered in columns. There are fewer questions in the test book than there are numbers on the answer sheet.

Make no stray marks on the answer sheet; they may count against you. You may use the margins of the test book for any scratch work, but you will **not** get credit for anything you write in the test book.

C) TEST BOOK

Sign your name on the line on the cover of this book and copy your candidate number into the appropriate boxes. If you do not have a candidate number, **print** your name under your signature.

Read each question carefully and choose the answer you think is **correct**. If you cannot decide on an answer to a question, go on to the next one and come back to this question later if you have time. Try to answer all questions. Marks are not subtracted for wrong answers. If you are not sure of an answer, it will be to your advantage to guess. It will probably be best to start at the beginning of the test book and work through the questions in order.

This examination contains a number of experimental questions being tested for future use. Your answers to these questions will **not** count toward your score. Because you will not be able to tell which questions are experimental, you should do your best on all questions, but do **not** spend too much time on any question.

The questions in the examination may be presented in cases or as independent questions. The context of some cases may seem similar to others in your test book. This reflects current practice where a practical nurse/nursing assistant may have to care for different clients with similar problems. Each case, however, tests different nursing content. The sample case on the next page shows the type of questions used. Correct answers are blackened in the ovals on the right.

SAMPLE CASE

Mr. Martin, 68 years old, is admitted to hospital with a diagnosis of pneumonia. The physician's orders include bedrest, oxygen therapy by mask, and incentive spirometer q. 1–2 h.

QUESTIONS 1 to 4 refer to this case.

1. Mr. Martin becomes upset when he learns he must stay in bed. Which one of the following approaches should the practical nurse/nursing assistant use when establishing a rapport with Mr. Martin?

    1. "Hello, Mr. Martin. I will be caring for you today and I am here to see that you follow the physician's orders."
    2. "Good morning, Mr. Martin. I hear you are unhappy about being put on bedrest."
    3. "Good morning, Mr. Martin. I understand you are upset about being on bedrest, but it's only for a few days."
    4. "Hello, Mr. Martin. I understand you have been put on bedrest. How do you feel about that?"

2. Mr. Martin is receiving oxygen as ordered. While changing his bed, the practical nurse/nursing assistant notices that the television has a frayed wire. Which one of the following actions should the practical nurse/nursing assistant take immediately?

    1. Turn off the oxygen and report the situation.
    2. Turn off and unplug the television, attach a "do not use" sign, and report the situation.
    3. Make arrangements to have Mr. Martin's television exchanged for one in safe working order.
    4. Caution Mr. Martin not to use the television until someone checks it.

3. The practical nurse/nursing assistant has been asked to assist Mr. Martin with his breathing and coughing exercises. Which one of the following interventions should the practical nurse/nursing assistant implement to promote his performance?

    1. Encourage Mr. Martin to inhale slowly and exhale rapidly.
    2. Instruct Mr. Martin to use his spirometer every hour.
    3. Ensure Mr. Martin is in a supine position when performing his breathing exercises.
    4. Explain to Mr. Martin that the best time to cough up secretions is in the evening before going to sleep.

4. Which one of the following interventions should the practical nurse/nursing assistant implement when providing mouth care for Mr. Martin?

    1. Ensure oral hygiene is completed every 2–3 hours.
    2. Wear sterile gloves.
    3. Provide mouthwash at the bedside.
    4. Keep the humidifier bottle filled with normal saline. ●②③④

END OF SAMPLE CASE

DO NOT GO TO THE NEXT PAGE OR BEGIN WORKING
UNTIL THE SIGNAL IS GIVEN TO DO SO

CASE 8

Mr. Henry, 25 years old, is transferred from the burn unit with partially healed burns to face, hands, and legs. The physician's orders include complete bedrest.

QUESTIONS 1 to 6 refer to this case.

1. On the initial visit, Mr. Henry states, "I'm ugly and there are so many things wrong with me." Which one of the following responses by the practical nurse/nursing assistant is most appropriate?
   1. "You're not ugly. I've seen many clients with more extensive burns." *disagreement, belittling concern*
   2. "I'm sure your family and friends will be accepting of your appearance." *false reassurance, misleading, unrealistic*
   3. "Let's take one thing at a time. It is important for you to talk about your feelings." *encourage expression of feelings*
   4. "Don't you worry. In no time you will look like you did before the accident." *false reassurance*

2. Later in the day, the practical nurse/nursing assistant finds Mr. Henry crying. Which one of the following interventions by the practical nurse/nursing assistant indicates an appropriate use of touch that would be therapeutic?
   1. Offering Mr. Henry a tissue *physical needs rather than emotional support*
   2. Placing a hand on Mr. Henry's shoulder *convey emotional support and acceptance*
   3. Putting a hand near Mr. Henry on his bed linens *message of avoidance*
   4. Wrapping an arm around Mr. Henry's waist *invasive, cause alienation of client*

3. Which one of the following diets should promote Mr. Henry's tissue growth, repair, and maintenance?
   1. High protein; low kilojoule (Calorie) *↓ kilojoule does not meet metabolic needs*
   2. Low protein; high kilojoule (Calorie)
   3. High protein; high kilojoule (Calorie) *↑ metabolic needs*
   4. Low protein; low kilojoule (Calorie)

4. The practical nurse/nursing assistant is formulating a teaching plan to reinforce Mr. Henry's diet regimen. Which one of the following interventions should the practical nurse/nursing assistant implement initially?
   1. Select the appropriate teaching aids.
   2. Assess Mr. Henry's level of knowledge.
   3. Research the necessary material regarding Mr. Henry's diet.
   4. Determine Mr. Henry's readiness to learn. *learning is not clear unless client is ready to learn*

5. Which one of the following observations by the practical nurse/nursing assistant indicates that Mr. Henry is likely experiencing fecal impaction?
  1. Frequent seepage of watery stool *liquid feces passes around the hardened stool*
  2. Passage of small, hard, and dry stool *sign of constipat²*
  3. Bouts of nausea and vomiting *N/V rarely associate c̄ fecal impaction*
  4. Elimination of black tarry stool *∴ disease process or ingestion of iron*

6. Mr. Henry is scheduled for a surgical debridement. He has refused to sign his consent form, stating that he does not understand the purpose of the surgery. Which one of the following actions must the practical nurse/nursing assistant take?
  1. Notify the nurse-in-charge.
  2. Explain the purpose of the surgery to Mr. Henry. *not explain it initial, can reinforce the purpose of surgery*
  3. Insist that Mr. Henry sign the consent form. *violate pt's right*
  4. Cancel Mr. Henry's surgery.

END OF CASE 8

CASE 9

Mrs. Pikes, 72 years old, has been readmitted to hospital with nephritis. Symptoms include flank pain, chills, fever, nausea and vomiting, and frequency with burning on voiding.

QUESTIONS 7 to 11 refer to this case.

7. *C & S* The physician orders a midstream urine for culture and sensitivity. In addition to having Mrs. Pikes wash her perineum with a cleansing soap, which one of the following procedures is the correct method for the practical nurse/nursing assistant to obtain the specimen?
  1. Have Mrs. Pikes empty her bladder into a sterile bedpan.
  2. Have Mrs. Pikes empty her bladder into a container with a preservative.
  3. Have Mrs. Pikes start to urinate in the toilet, stop urinating, and continue to urinate into a clean bedpan.
  4. Have Mrs. Pikes start to urinate in the toilet, stop urinating, and continue to urinate into a sterile container. *midway urine sterile container*

53

8. The physician has ordered catheter drainage. Which of the following interventions by the practical nurse/nursing assistant best describe perineal care with an indwelling catheter?

    1. Scrub the perineum, catheter, and tubing with warm water and an antiseptic soap. *lead to skin breakdown* *bunny to perineum* *not necessary*

    2. Delicately wash the perineum with hot water and a mild soap, beginning with the urinary meatus while separating the labia.

    3. Gently wash the perineum with warm water and a mild soap, separate the labia, and cleanse around the meatus and down the tubing about 10 cm. *principle of medical asepsis*

    4. Carefully wash the perineum with soap and water, separate the labia, and cleanse up and down the perineum and tubing about 10 cm. *should clean in downward direction* *may introduce bacteria into bladder*

9. When ambulating Mrs. Pikes, which one of the following interventions by the practical nurse/nursing assistant maintains continuous urinary catheter drainage?

    1. Tie the drainage bag to the dressing gown's belt.
    2. Hold the drainage bag at knee level. *lower than bladder position*
    3. Coil the drainage tubing in Mrs. Pikes' hand.
    4. Carry the coiled drainage tubing for Mrs. Pikes. *disrupt flow of urine by having*

10. Mrs. Pikes' physician has ordered increased fluids for her. Which one of the following actions by the practical nurse/nursing assistant is most appropriate to meet the new order?

    1. Notify the food service department. *not food service's responsibility*
    2. Request that the family make sure Mrs. Pikes drinks more fluids. *not family's resp.*
    3. Order a clear liquid diet. *have nutrient.*
    4. Offer fluids to Mrs. Pikes at mealtime and between meals. *at regular, frequent intervals*

11. Mrs. Pikes' catheter has been removed. Which one of the following interventions by the practical nurse/nursing assistant is most appropriate to promote bladder retraining?

    1. Increase fluid intake. *not necessarily bladder retraining*
    2. Enforce n.p.o. *not indicated*
    3. Observe for bladder distention. *only if indicate urinary retention*
    4. Schedule elimination times. *promote bladder muscle control*

END OF CASE 9

CASE 10

Mrs. Bradley, a debilitated 85-year-old client, has been admitted to hospital for pain control and bedrest.

QUESTIONS 12 to 15 refer to this case.

12. Which one of the following behaviors by Mrs. Bradley indicates to the practical nurse/nursing assistant that the client may be experiencing pain?
    1. She speaks very rapidly and wrings her hands. *indicates nervousness*
    2. She refuses to make eye contact and cries easily. *depression*
    3. She grimaces and holds herself rigidly in one position. *pain observed through facial express"*
    4. She cuddles her doll and refers to it as her "baby." *comfortable*

13. Which one of the following measures performed by the practical nurse/nursing assistant is most effective in the prevention of decubitus ulcers for Mrs. Bradley?
    1. Bathing Mrs. Bradley twice a day using a medicated soap. *promote skin breakdown — not preventing decubitus ulcers*
    2. Bathing Mrs. Bradley daily using bath oil. *bathing elderly daily not advised*
    3. Massaging reddened bony areas with lotion after turning Mrs. Bradley. *not and promote skin breakdown not preventing*
    4. Assisting Mrs. Bradley, if necessary, to turn every 2 hours. *pressure on vulnerable areas*

14. Which one of the following responses by the practical nurse/nursing assistant is most appropriate when Mrs. Bradley states, "I'm in so much pain and I'm too old for this. I wish I was dead!" *negates clients feeling*
    1. "Don't talk like that, Mrs. Bradley. You have so much to be thankful for."
    2. "I'll come back later, Mrs. Bradley, when you are in a better mood." *avoidance, closing to problems*
    3. "You seem upset, Mrs. Bradley. Tell me more about how you are feeling." *shows empathy, warmth and interest, open for discussion*
    4. "Your physician will be in this afternoon. You can discuss this then if you like." *pass problem to sb else*

15. Mrs. Bradley's physician has ordered that her fluid intake and output be monitored. Which of the following items should the practical nurse/nursing assistant record on the intake and output sheet? *liquid item*
    1. Green beans, mashed potatoes, and tomato juice
    2. Raspberry gelatin, consomme soup, and water
    3. Apple juice, oatmeal, and toast *not a liquid item*
    4. Beef stew, milkshake, and canned peaches

not

END OF CASE 10

GO TO NEXT PAGE

CASE 11

Mr. Thom Woods, 27 years old, has AIDS. He was admitted to hospital with dehydration and exhaustion.

QUESTIONS 16 to 21 refer to this case.

16. The practical nurse's/nursing assistant's co-workers are discussing Mr. Woods' case in the coffee lounge. Which one of the following initial actions by the practical nurse/nursing assistant is most appropriate?
    1. Remind the co-workers about confidentiality.
    2. Inform Mr. Woods that his case is being discussed. *upset client*
    3. Report the incident to the nurse-in-charge. *only if they fail to adhere confidenti guidelin*
    4. Suggest an inservice program on confidentiality. ✓ *if problem continue. but not dealing ō immediate problem*

17. Which one of the following manifestations is an early indicator of potential skin breakdown in Mr. Woods?
    1. Reddened tissue
    2. Numbness *later manifestations of skin breakdown*
    3. A broken blister *damage has already taken place*
    4. Excoriation *skin breakdown has already occurred*

18. During routine morning care, the practical nurse/nursing assistant notices a reddened area on Mr. Woods' sacrum. Which one of the following measures should the practical nurse/nursing assistant implement?
    1. Encourage him to rest as much as possible. *should be as mobile as possible*
    2. Massage the reddened area. *only promote skin breakdown*
    3. Reposition him every 2 hours.
    4. Apply a moist compress. *not required ∴ no evidence of skin breakdown*

19. Which one of the following measures should the practical nurse/nursing assistant implement to promote relaxation and sleep for Mr. Woods?
    1. Encourage his friends to visit. *should monitor no. of visitors, already exhausted*
    2. Monitor his outgoing phone calls. *not respecting pt's rights*
    3. Reorganize his nursing care. *can minimize interruptions and provide a restful environment*
    4. Recommend sleep medication. *only after other methods have been tried*

20. Mr. Woods is placed on I.V. therapy. Which of the following observations should indicate to the practical nurse/nursing assistant that Mr. Woods' I.V. is now interstitial?
    1. Edema and pallor at the site *infiltration*
    2. Redness and pain at the site *phlebitis*
    3. Increased flow rate and pallor at the site *flow rate usu. ↓ if infiltration occurs*
    4. Redness and leakage at the site *leakage may occur in infiltration, but not redness*

21. Which one of the following measures should the practical nurse/nursing assistant take to assist Mr. Woods in recording his fluid intake and output?
    1. Provide him with a fluid conversion chart. *easy, accurate method for recording*
    2. Remind him to drink plenty of fluids. *not recording*
    3. Encourage him to record all I.V. therapy. *pt has no idea about IV therapy*
    4. Remind him to record all pureed foods. *pureed food is not considered fluid, and is not recorded.*

END OF CASE 11

CASE 12

Joan Mills, 25 years old, is admitted to the hospital with low back pain.

QUESTIONS 22 to 27 refer to this case.

22. As part of the admission procedure for Ms. Mills, which one of the following interventions is the responsibility of the practical nurse/nursing assistant?
    1. Orient Ms. Mills to the unit. *↓ anxiety , within scope of practice*
    2. Notify the family physician. *resp. of RN*
    3. Obtain and test a blood specimen. *resp. of lab technician*
    4. Ensure complete bedrest. *not a component of admission procedure.*

23. After completing the nursing history with Ms. Mills, which one of the following data must the practical nurse/nursing assistant report immediately to the registered nurse?
    1. Independent mobility
    2. An allergy to milk *not an immediate concern*
    3. Blood pressure of 120/80 mmHg
    4. Numbness of the right leg *immediate problem, safety.*

57

24. Which one of the following behaviors by the practical nurse/nursing assistant should indicate to Ms. Mills that the practical nurse/nursing assistant is listening attentively to her?

1. Crosses arms *defensive position*
2. Minimizes eye contact *unwilling to listen*
3. Writes detailed notes *writing should be kept min. c̄ listening to pt.*
4. Maintains an open posture *encourage communication*

25. The physiotherapist has taught Ms. Mills a series of exercises to strengthen her back muscles. Which one of the following interventions by the practical nurse/nursing assistant is most appropriate?

1. Encourage Ms. Mills to perform the exercises as prescribed.
2. Perform passive exercises for Ms. Mills when she becomes tired. *passive exercise not producing same result of active exercise*
3. Modify the exercises according to Ms. Mills' preferences. *must not b̄ā s consultation of physio.*
4. Have Ms. Mills perform the exercises until she experiences pain. *exercise should not cause pain.*

26. Which one of the following strategies should the practical nurse/nursing assistant use to assist Ms. Mills to cope with her back pain? *should be avoid s̄ c̄ back pain*

1. Suggest that she lie in a prone position. *precipitate complications immobility*
2. Encourage her to remain in the most comfortable position.
3. Ask her about previously successful pain management techniques. *use pt's relief measu often work best*
4. Discuss with her the use of a lumbosacral brace. *require Dr's order, not for long-term use ∴ restricts mov't. causes weakening of back muscles.*

27. While assisting Ms. Mills to get out of bed, the practical nurse/nursing assistant takes the opportunity to teach her about proper body mechanics. Which one of the following instructions should be included?

1. When sitting, avoid keeping the knees level with the hips. *knees should be kept level hips c̄ sitting*
2. When lifting, avoid twisting at the waist. *put stress on back*
3. When bending, keep the feet together. *require wide of base of support*
4. When sitting, prop the back with pillows. *should be supported in a straight-backed chair not c̄ pillow*

END OF CASE 12

58

CASE 13

Anna Reese, 70 years old, has been admitted to hospital with a diagnosis of chronic obstructive pulmonary disease. She is dyspneic and is receiving continuous oxygen at 2 L/min by nasal cannula.

QUESTIONS 28 to 33 refer to this case.

28. Which one of the following interventions by the practical nurse/nursing assistant is required to ensure correct oxygen administration for Mrs. Reese?
    1. Check that the flow rate is maintained. *regular check of flow rate*
    2. Lubricate the cannula tips with water before insertion. *could result in choking - inhaled*
    3. Fill the humidification container with tap water. *sterile water* *moisture*
    4. Adjust the headband to fit tightly over the ears. *tight fit causes tissue damage over ears*

29. Which one of the following findings should be reported by the practical nurse/nursing assistant as an objective manifestation of dyspnea in Mrs. Reese?
    1. Persistent chest pain
    2. Frequent dizziness *Subjective*
    3. Intercostal muscle use
    4. Increased thirst

30. Which one of the following descriptors regarding Mrs. Reese is the best example of clear documentation by the practical nurse/nursing assistant?
    1. Sharp, left-sided chest pain *nature, location of pain*
    2. Difficulty breathing at mealtime *subjective*
    3. Pain when getting out of bed *time of pain, not nature*
    4. Dryness from the nasal cannula *location not specific*

31. Mrs. Reese states, "I get so scared when I can't breathe properly because I think I am going to die." Which one of the following responses by the practical nurse/nursing assistant is most appropriate? *enhance communication, leave direction to client.*
    1. "Tell me more about the feelings you described."
    2. "This is a normal response to your condition." *belittling concern*
    3. "The oxygen you receive will keep you breathing." *not address to fear*
    4. "Why do you feel that you are going to die?" *why Q threatening*

59

32. In which one of the following positions would Mrs. Reese be most comfortable?
    1. Side-lying with her uppermost arm and leg supported on pillows *Not best c̄ dyspnea*
    2. Semi-Fowler's with pillows under her arms and lower legs *not adequately c̄ dyspnea*
    3. Dorsal recumbent with pillows under her arms and ankles *moderate dyspnea*
    4. High-Fowler's with pillows under her arms and at her feet
       enhance breathing, increase comfort

33. Mrs. Reese is being discharged tomorrow. Which one of the following interventions by the practical nurse/nursing assistant is most beneficial for Mrs. Reese?
    1. Stress the importance of avoiding crowds in flu season. *avoid contact of infection URT in COPD pe.*
    2. Suggest she use elastic support stockings.
    3. Encourage a moderate restriction in fluid intake. *fluid be ↑ rather than ↓ to liquify secretions*
    4. Increase the oxygen flow rate if her dyspnea intensifies. *not advised*

END OF CASE 13

CASE 14

Mr. Snow, a 65-year-old who smokes, is newly admitted to the hospital with a diagnosis of congestive heart failure. Mr. Snow has a urinary catheter in place and will undergo various tests.

QUESTIONS 34 to 39 refer to this case.

34. Which one of the following principles should the practical nurse/nursing assistant consider when assessing Mr. Snow's blood pressure?
    1. A chronic volume deficit increases blood pressure. *↓ BP*
    2. Blood pressure varies over the course of the day. *lowest in am. highest later in the day*
    3. Syncope occurs with elevated blood pressure. *c̄ ↓ BP*
    4. Blood pressure tends to decrease with age.

35. Mr. Snow is scheduled for an electrocardiogram. Which one of the following assessments is most appropriate for the practical nurse/nursing assistant to make?
    1. Monitor Mr. Snow for signs of intestinal bleeding. *no internal bleeding would occur c̄ ECG*
    2. Assess the puncture site for bleeding. *no puncture site*
    3. Assess Mr. Snow's anxiety level. *assessment to impact of anxiety is important particularly in cardiac patient*
    4. Monitor Mr. Snow's pedal pulses. *pedal pulses not affected by ECG*

60

36. Which one of the following actions by Mr. Snow indicates that he understands how to care for his indwelling catheter? *contraindicated ∴ risk for microorganism growth*
    1. He applies lotion to perineal skin folds.
    +2. He carries the catheter bag at waist level.
    3. He reduces his intake of fluids at bedtime. *should ↑ ∴ flushing the urinary tract*
    (4.) He removes encrusted material around the meatus.
    ∴ collection of material leads to urethral irritation / infection

37. Which one of the following interventions should the practical nurse/nursing assistant implement to help Mr. Snow maintain a restricted fluid intake?
    1. Schedule all fluids to be taken with his meals. *b/w meals*
    2. Provide fluids in a large clear container. *use small container ↓ desire for fluid*
    (3.) Offer ice chips as an alternative to liquids. *good alternative calculated as ½ g frozen volume*
    4. Emphasize repeatedly the total fluids allowed. *results in frustration*

38. Which one of the following instructions should the practical nurse/nursing assistant give to Mr. Snow about his special foot care needs?
    (1.) Apply elastic support stockings daily. *requires Dr's order. care for venous congestion, not felt*
    2. Soak his feet in hot water. *not recom.*
    3. Wear loose fitting slippers. *dangerous.*
    (4.) Inspect his feet daily.

39. The physician has recommended to Mr. Snow that he quit smoking. Which one of the following interventions by the practical nurse/nursing assistant would best help Mr. Snow understand the importance of quitting smoking?
    (1.) Discuss the risk factors associated with smoking. *not focus on heart problem*
    2. Identify the changes he can expect if he does not quit smoking. *not describing reasons.*
    3. Assist him to create a schedule to reduce the frequency of his smoking. *not help understand reasons for quitting*
    (4.) Use a cardiac video to discuss the effects that smoking has on the heart.

END OF CASE 14

INDEPENDENT QUESTIONS

QUESTIONS 40 to 103 do not refer to a case.

40. The practical nurse/nursing assistant finds several pills on the bathroom sink in a four-bed room of a surgical unit. Which of the following actions must the practical nurse/nursing assistant take?
1. Ask each client if they left their pills on the bathroom sink. *unsafe practice*
2. Leave the pills on the bathroom sink and report the incident to the nurse-in-charge. *unsafe violate resp.*
3. Note the color of the pills and dispose of them down the toilet. *not help identifying pt.*
4. Give the nurse-in-charge the pills and a report of the incident. *permit possible identification of owner of pills proper practice to fill in an incident report.*

41. Which one of the following rationales best describes why the practical nurse/nursing assistant should wear disposable gloves when providing perineal care?
1. To maintain universal precautions *prevent cross contaminat?*
2. To decrease the frequency of handwashing *not a substitute for handwashing. wash hands before/after applying g*
3. To maintain sterility
4. To protect the client

42. During the admission procedure of 2-year-old Tammy, the practical nurse/nursing assistant asks Tammy's mother if she has a favorite toy. Which one of the following statements best describes the benefits a favorite toy can offer? *help assoc. c the familiar, givig feelig of security*
1. The toy provides security for Tammy while she is in unfamiliar surroundings.
2. The toy diverts Tammy and keeps her quieter on the unit. *toy not nece kept her quiet*
3. The toy helps Tammy make friends more easily. *toy not gaurantee socializat?*
4. The toy encourages Tammy to participate in play activities. *not ensure participat? in play activit'es*

43. Which one of the following interventions should the practical nurse/nursing assistant implement initially when giving a client an enema?
1. Place the client in a side-lying position. *not initial though appropriate*
2. Verify the physician's order.
3. Provide for privacy.
4. Explain the procedure.

62

A9-9997

44. Mr. Jones, 75 years old and 119 kg, recently suffered a cerebrovascular accident and now must be transferred using a mechanical lift. Which one of the following interventions should the practical nurse/nursing assistant implement first before using the lift to transfer Mr. Jones from his bed to a chair?
    1. Check the sling and straps for fraying.
    2. Position the top of the sling under Mr. Jones' shoulders.
    3. Fold Mr. Jones's arms across his chest.
    4. Ensure the bed is in the lowest position with the head raised.

45. Ryan, 16 years old, has muscular dystrophy and is bedridden. The practical nurse/nursing assistant would like to prevent abduction of Ryan's legs while in the supine position. Which one of the following positioning aides should the practical nurse/nursing assistant use?
    1. A foot cradle
    2. Sandbags between Ryan's legs
    3. Trochanter rolls bilaterally
    4. A footboard

46. Jason, 14 years old, has been admitted to the pediatric unit with a diagnosis of depression. The practical nurse/nursing assistant notices that he has given away several of his T-shirts to other children on the unit. Which one of the following actions must the practical nurse/nursing assistant take initially?
    1. Document the observation on his chart.
    2. Report the behavior to the nurse-in-charge.
    3. Inform Jason's mother.
    4. Observe Jason for the next few days.

47. A male client, 18 years old, has just been hospitalized for reassessment of insulin dependent (Type I) diabetes mellitus, diagnosed 2 years ago. He is not being compliant with the diet ordered. Which one of the following statements by the practical nurse/nursing assistant would be most appropriate during a team conference held to assess the client's nutritional needs and attitude toward his diet?
    1. "Dr. Brown should be asked to explain the risks of noncompliance to him."
    2. "I suggest the dietitian should be contacted to discuss menu selection."
    3. "I think we need to ask him why he chooses to be noncompliant."
    4. "The client should be allowed to experience the consequences of his behavior."

63

48. Shawna, 10 years old, has joint discomfort in her left elbow, for which moist compresses have been ordered. Which one of the following interventions by the practical nurse/nursing assistant demonstrates a good understanding of medical aseptic technique when applying compresses to Shawna's elbow?

    1. Applies a moist compress using sterile gloves
    2. Uses nonsterile gloves to apply a moist compress   *∴ no break in skin integrity*
    3. Uses sterile forceps to apply a moist compress
    4. Applies a moist compress with clean hands   *intact integument*

49. A practical nurse/nursing assistant is asked to do a blood pressure check on Ms. Jones, a new client. Which one of the following approaches indicates that the practical nurse/nursing assistant is aware of the proper method of verifying a client's name?

    1. "Hello. Are you Ms. Jones?"
    2. "Hello. You must be the new client, Ms. Jones."
    3. "Hello, Ms. Jones. May I check your identification band?"
    4. "Hello, Ms. Jones. I am here to check your blood pressure."

50. Bobby, 6 years old, has been confined to bed for 1 week with leg traction. To date, he has not had visitors. Which one of the following measures should the practical nurse/nursing assistant take to increase the opportunity for Bobby to interact socially?

    1. Take Bobby in his bed to the playroom.   *Can initiate immediately and give him opportunity to interact ī other chi*
    2. Encourage Bobby's family to visit.   *∮ in social interactⁿ*
    3. Call the school and have Bobby's teacher send homework.   *only a diversional activ's*
    4. Arrange for Bobby to watch television in his room.

51. Which one of the following interventions is a responsibility of the practical nurse/nursing assistant in preparing an elderly male client for hip surgery?

    1. Inform him of the possible complications and risks of having surgery.   *Surgeon's respo*
    2. Instruct him on the effects of his preoperative medications.   *resp. of RN who gives med*
    3. Explain to him what equipment and activities to expect postoperatively.
    4. Have him empty his bladder completely after receiving his preoperative medication.   *void before preop med.*
    ∴ safty
    relaxing effect of med.   *lightheadedness / drowsiness*

52. Mr. Grey, 60 years old, recently had a stroke. He has difficulty dressing himself. Which one of the following responses by the practical nurse/nursing assistant best promotes Mr. Grey's independence?

    1. "Your schedule has been rearranged to allow you extra time to dress yourself."   *assumed a prob*
    2. "Let's set up a contract outlining when you will dress yourself."   *demanding independence*
    3. "Dressing yourself will make you feel so much better."   *not promote independency*
    4. "Which item would you like me to assist you with?"
    allow pt to make decision on
    · which item
    · assistance required

64

53. Ms. Green is scheduled for a <u>cleansing enema</u> prior to her barium series. Ms. Green states, "I don't really think I need this enema." Which one of the following statements should the practical nurse/nursing assistant make? *inappropriate alternative*

1. "I realize enemas are uncomfortable. Would you rather have a suppository?"
2. "I know that the procedure can be <u>uncomfortable</u>, but it is <u>necessary for the best</u> viewing during your barium test." *accept concern, provide explanat⁼.*
3. "That is your decision, but we will have to cancel the barium test if you refuse the enema." *judgemental, blaming client*
4. "It's only an enema. It will be over before you know it." *belittle concern, no decision making*

54. As a result of a cerebrovascular <u>accident 2 years ago</u>, *CVA* <u>54-year-old</u> Mrs. Jacson is <u>aphasic</u> and has <u>left hemiplegia</u>. Mrs. Jacson has been admitted to a long-term care facility for respite care. How should the practical nurse/nursing assistant assess how much assistance Mrs. Jacson will require with her activities of daily living?

1. Ask Mrs. Jacson how much assistance she will require.
2. Give her a wash basin and observe her actions.
3. Check the discharge summary from the hospital. *at home, not in hospital*
4. Consult with Mr. Jacson, who has been caring for her at home. *most reliable source of informat⁼*

55. Mrs. Green refuses to have her leg dressing changed. Which one of the following responses by the practical nurse/nursing assistant is most appropriate?

1. "Changing the dressing is painful. I will schedule a pain medication for your comfort." *assume problem to pain*
2. "The physician has ordered your dressing change today." *minimize concern*
3. "Tell me how having your dressing changed affects you." *encourage openly discuss feeling*
4. "The dressing is quite involved and this specific time allows us not to rush." *& decision making on pts part*

56. Molly Sangster, <u>18</u> years old, has <u>paralysis of her left arm</u>. Her mother asks why the practical nurse/nursing assistant continues to exercise Molly's left arm and hand. Which one of the following responses by the practical nurse/nursing assistant is most appropriate?

1. "This exercise is useful in maintaining joint flexibility in the limb."
2. "This exercise was ordered by the physician and must be implemented twice daily." *not explaining why*
3. "This exercise increases the muscle strength and will enhance the return of function of the limb." *passive ex. will not ↑ muscle strength*
4. "This is an isotonic exercise and will reduce shortening of the muscles in the limb." *isotonic ex. need contract⁼ of muscles is not passive ex.*

57. Edna Blain, a bedridden 85-year-old client, has long hair which becomes tangled easily. Which one of the following interventions by the practical nurse/nursing assistant is most appropriate when providing hair care for this client?

1. Tie her hair back with a colorful ribbon. *ø Client input*
2. Secure her hair in a braid around her head. *"*
3. Style her hair according to her wishes. *right to participate in care*
4. Suggest that she consider cutting her hair. *Uncomfortable decision making situation)*

58. Beth, 16 years old, is unconscious after being involved in a motor vehicle accident. In which one of the following positions should the practical nurse/nursing assistant place Beth when performing mouth care?

1. Prone position *ø access to oral cavity*
2. Side-lying position *allow secret? to drain, prevent aspirat?*
3. Semi-Fowler's position *secret? collects in back of throat. Could aspira*
4. Position of comfort *primary: ↓ risk of aspiration*

59. Which one of the following interventions should the practical nurse/nursing assistant implement initially for a client who has been pronounced dead?

1. Place the body on a shroud. *after family visit*
2. Remove all jewelry. *before family leaves so they can take home*
3. Collect the client's personal effects. *after family viewing*
4. Prepare the body for family viewing.

60. Dave, 13 years old, has a fracture in his dominant arm. In addition to placing his tray close by, which of the following interventions should the practical nurse/nursing assistant implement to assist him with his meal?

assist + allow independence

1. Place items for easy access.
2. Allow him to proceed independently. *Pt need assistance to prepare tray*
3. Ask him the order in which he would like the foods. *Not promote independence*
4. Feed him, offering the most nutritious items first.

61. Marcus, 15 years old, has had an inguinal hernia repair. Which one of the following measures should the practical nurse/nursing assistant suggest to Marcus to maintain regular elimination? *do not promote regular elim.*

1. Encourage Marcus to select dairy products.
2. Provide fluids and encourage Marcus to drink. *healthy elimnt? facilitated y daily intake of fluids 6-8 glasses/(*
3. Tell Marcus to go to the washroom every 4 hours.
4. Instruct Marcus on the regular use of laxatives.

not the role of PN to instruct pt to use laxatives

66

A9-9997

62. Which one of the following occasions is the best time for the practical nurse/nursing assistant to begin discharge planning? *to meet changing needs.*
    1. On admission
    2. On the day of discharge *∅ meeting pt need*
    3. Upon request of the family *Can be initiated before family discussion*
    4. With the physician's order *not required for discharge planning*

63. An 18-year-old female client is having difficulty controlling the odor from her colostomy. Which one of the following interventions by the practical nurse/nursing assistant is most appropriate for meeting this client's needs?
    1. Ensure that she understands which foods cause odor. *effective way to control odor*
    2. Encourage her to change the appliance more often.
    3. Suggest that she use an appliance deodorizer regularly. *Could cause stoma irritation*
    4. Provide her with the latest equipment in stoma care. *may not solve odor problem*

64. The practical nurse/nursing assistant observes Mr. Black, 65 years old, cleaning his dentures. Which one of the following actions by Mr. Black demonstrates to the practical nurse/nursing assistant the need for client teaching?
    1. He stores the dentures in cool water. *denture moist, insertion easier*
    2. He rinses the dentures in hot water.
    3. He removes the dentures for cleaning.
    4. He places a towel in the basin. *↓ chance of breakage.*

65. A 30-year-old female client is performing a sterile dressing change on her surgical incision. Which one of the following observations by the practical nurse/nursing assistant indicates that this client understands the principles of surgical asepsis?
    1. She pats her wound dry with her bath towel after showering.
    2. She first cleans along the incision line *fm least contaminated to most contaminated*
    3. She washes her hands after changing the dressing.
    4. She avoids picking at and touching her dressing. *avoid contamination not a surgical aseptic practice*

66. James Tye, an obese 30-year-old with a spastic muscular disorder, is on bedrest with commode privileges. While visiting with relatives, he asks to use the commode for the first time. Which one of the following interventions by the practical nurse/nursing assistant is most appropriate in responding to James' request?
    1. Transfer James after explaining how he can be of assistance. *weight/condition critical*
    2. Transfer James with the assistance of one of his relatives. *unsafe ∴ untrained*
    3. Place James in a mechanical lifting device to transfer him.
    4. Request the assistance of a nursing co-worker. *Safe, weight/condition.*

67

67. Which one of the following actions by the practical nurse/nursing assistant would best assist an adult client to regain bladder control?
    1. Place the client's call bell within easy reach.
    2. Offer drinks that contain caffeine.
    3. Identify the target date on the calendar.
    4. Monitor elimination patterns. *so as to develop a voiding schedule*

68. Mr. Jensen, 62 years old, has fallen down the stairs at the nursing home. The practical nurse/nursing assistant notices a large laceration on Mr. Jensen's mid-forearm with extensive bleeding. Which one of the following interventions by the practical nurse/nursing assistant is the most appropriate initially?
    1. Apply direct pressure to the wound.
    2. Place a cold pack over the wound. *not recommended*
    3. Apply pressure at the brachial site. *↓ blood flow to entire arm*
    4. Elevate the arm above heart level. *not initial act'n*

69. Which one of the following statements by the practical nurse/nursing assistant indicates an understanding of the purpose of applying antiembolic stockings for a client on bedrest?
    1. "The stockings exert pressure on the veins, promoting venous blood flow to the heart." *↓ venous blood pooling   enhance venous blood return to h*
    2. "The stockings constrict the veins, impeding venous blood flow to the heart." *promot.*
    3. "The stockings permit range-of-motion exercises, promoting venous blood flow to the heart." *not affect performance of ROM ex.*
    4. "The stockings prevent muscles from contracting, impeding venous blood flow to the heart." *not prevent muscle contraction*

70. Which one of the following devices should the practical nurse/nursing assistant use to help prevent hip dislocation in a 54-year-old male client with hemiplegia?
    1. A footboard *prevent plantar flexion / footdrop*
    2. A trochanter roll *prevent external rotation of hips*
    3. An alternating pressure mattress *relieve pressure*
    4. A sheepskin *comfort measure*

71. A 16-year-old male client has a full-length cast on his right leg. Which one of the following activities should the practical nurse/nursing assistant carry out in assisting him in the use of crutches?
    1. Remind him to support his body weight on his axillae when standing with the crutches. *not to support weight on axilla*
    2. Remind him to place his left foot on a stair before moving the crutches when ascending. *affected leg always supported by crutches*
    3. Advise him to make adjustments to the length of his crutches according to the shoes he wears.
    4. Walk beside him on his unaffected side as he uses the crutches.

should walk slightly behind pt on the affected side.

72. Stephen Foxe, 20 years old, has insulin dependent (Type I) diabetes mellitus. Which one of the following behaviors best indicates to the practical nurse/nursing assistant that Stephen is assuming responsibility for his own health?

    1. He attempts to remove both physical and psychological stress from his life. *not possible*
    2. He regularly attends teaching sessions sponsored by the Canadian Diabetes Association. *taking active role in health promotion strategy*
    3. He regularly asks a family member to give him his insulin injections.
    4. He checks his feet for sores and cracks in the skin on a weekly basis. *should daily basis*

73. The practical nurse/nursing assistant is assessing 10-year-old Melissa's full-leg cast. Which one of the following observations must the practical nurse/nursing assistant report immediately?

    1. Toes are pale and cool. *impaired blood flow*
    2. Capillary refill is present.
    3. Toes are pink and warm.
    4. Itching is present. *needs only a comfortable measures*

74. The practical nurse/nursing assistant notices Emily, 14 years old, sitting in the waiting room with her head in her hands, sobbing. Which one of the following actions by the practical nurse/nursing assistant demonstrates good communication skills in dealing with this situation?

    1. Sits next to Emily and states, "Don't cry, everything will be OK." *false reassurance*
    2. Does not disturb Emily at this time *benefit for intervention*
    3. Reports the incident to the nurse-in-charge *not providing emotional support*
    4. Approaches Emily and asks, "May I sit with you?" *support to availability*

75. Which one of the following instructions should the practical nurse/nursing assistant provide to a new mother regarding bottle feeding?

    1. Formula should be freshly prepared before each feeding. *24h supply is safe*
    2. The infant should be burped or bubbled during the feeding. *get rid of excessive swallow air*
    3. The nipple hole should be enlarged to produce a stream of formula. *to avoid choking*
    4. The baby may be fed by propping the bottle. *lead to aspiration/choking/blocking airway*

76. The practical nurse/nursing assistant observes a female client with peripheral vascular disease (PVD) walking in bare feet, and the practical nurse/nursing assistant tells her she should be wearing appropriate footwear. Which one of the following reasons best describes the rationale for the practical nurse's/nursing assistant's statement?

    1. The client may fall due to the fact she will have frequent dizzy spells from PVD.
    2. The client may injure her feet and they will heal poorly due to PVD. *↓ circulation*
    3. The floor is cold and the client may further decrease circulation to her feet. *safety 1st, not comfort*
    4. The client with PVD needs the support offered by the footwear. *protect, not support*

69

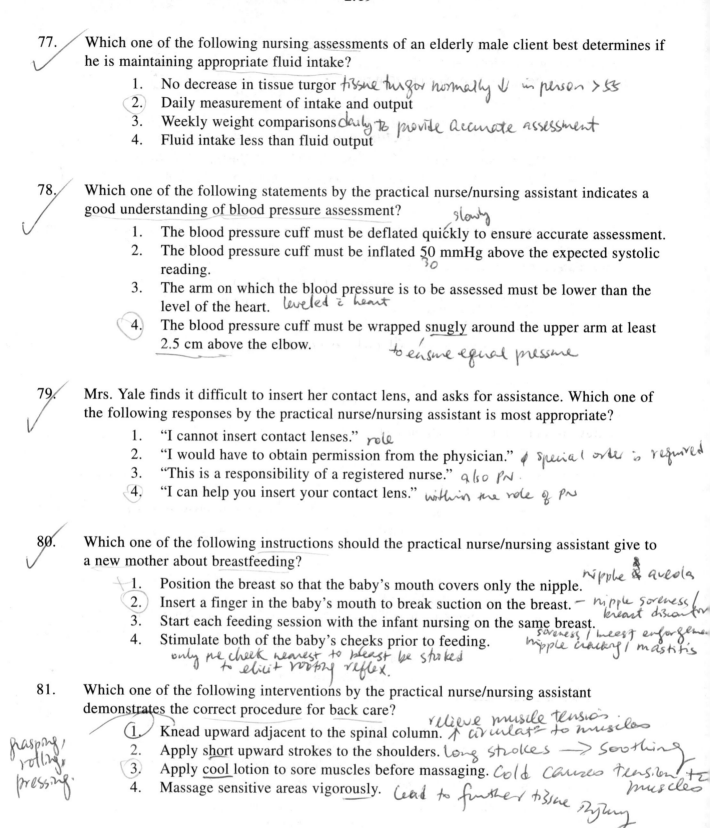

77. Which one of the following nursing assessments of an elderly male client best determines if he is maintaining appropriate fluid intake?

   1. No decrease in tissue turgor *tissue turgor normally ↓ in person >55*
   (2.) Daily measurement of intake and output
   3. Weekly weight comparisons *daily to provide accurate assessment*
   4. Fluid intake less than fluid output

78. Which one of the following statements by the practical nurse/nursing assistant indicates a good understanding of blood pressure assessment?

   1. The blood pressure cuff must be deflated quickly to ensure accurate assessment. *slowly*
   2. The blood pressure cuff must be inflated 50 mmHg above the expected systolic reading. *30*
   3. The arm on which the blood pressure is to be assessed must be lower than the level of the heart. *leveled c̄ heart*
   (4.) The blood pressure cuff must be wrapped snugly around the upper arm at least 2.5 cm above the elbow. *to ensure equal pressure*

79. Mrs. Yale finds it difficult to insert her contact lens, and asks for assistance. Which one of the following responses by the practical nurse/nursing assistant is most appropriate?

   1. "I cannot insert contact lenses." *role*
   2. "I would have to obtain permission from the physician." *∅ special order is required*
   3. "This is a responsibility of a registered nurse." *also PN.*
   (4.) "I can help you insert your contact lens." *within the role of PN*

80. Which one of the following instructions should the practical nurse/nursing assistant give to a new mother about breastfeeding?

   1. Position the breast so that the baby's mouth covers only the nipple. *nipple & areola*
   (2.) Insert a finger in the baby's mouth to break suction on the breast. *— nipple soreness / breast distortion*
   3. Start each feeding session with the infant nursing on the same breast. *soreness / breast engorgement*
   4. Stimulate both of the baby's cheeks prior to feeding. *nipple cracking / mastitis*
   only the cheek nearest to breast be stroked to elicit rooting reflex.

81. Which one of the following interventions by the practical nurse/nursing assistant demonstrates the correct procedure for back care?

   (1.) Knead upward adjacent to the spinal column. *relieve muscle tension ↑ circulation to muscles*
   2. Apply short upward strokes to the shoulders. *long strokes → soothing*
   3. Apply cool lotion to sore muscles before massaging. *Cold causes tension to muscles*
   4. Massage sensitive areas vigorously. *Lead to further tissue injury*

grasping, rolling, pressing.

70

82. Upon entering the room, the practical nurse/nursing assistant finds Mrs. James lying on the floor. The side rail on her bed is down, she has a small bruise on her left elbow, and the physician has been notified. Which of the following entries should the practical nurse/nursing assistant include in the documentation?

1. Client found lying on the floor and bruised her elbow. The side rail had been left down. Physician notified.
2. Client fell out of bed and bruised her elbow. Physician notified.
3. Client found lying on the floor. Small bruise noted on left elbow. Physician notified. *entered objectively*
4. Client fell out of bed this morning. Small bruising noted on left elbow.

83. The fire alarm rings while Mrs. Biggs, a 78-year-old client with Alzheimer disease, is sitting in the hallway a considerable distance from her room. Which one of the following actions by the practical nurse/nursing assistant is most appropriate?

1. Instruct Mrs. Biggs to return to her room.
2. Ask a volunteer to remain with Mrs. Biggs.
3. Assist Mrs. Biggs to the nearest room. *quickest to ensure safety*
4. Help Mrs. Biggs to her room.

84. Mr. Ray, 64 years old, had a transurethral resection of the prostate and is on continuous bladder irrigation. Which one of the following interventions should the practical nurse/nursing assistant implement to maintain universal precautions while emptying the drainage bag?

1. Ensure that the drain port does not touch the measurement container. *not principle of universal precaut.*
2. Use a large sterile syringe to empty the drainage bag. *incorrect*
3. Clean the drainage port before emptying the drainage bag. *not universal precaution*
4. Wear clean gloves to unclamp and empty the drainage bag. *Contact c blood/body fluid*

85. Which one of the following measures should the practical nurse/nursing assistant take when changing an ostomy appliance?

1. Plan to change the appliance 30 minutes before meals. *affect appetite*
2. Peel the drainage bag off the skin quickly. *↑ discomfort / skin breakdown*
3. Rub the skin to remove any debris. *Skin breakdown*
4. Place the client in a standing or lying position. *permit easier application prevent spilling contents*

86. An adolescent male client was unconscious for 5 minutes following a bicycle accident. Which of the following observations should indicate to the practical nurse/nursing assistant that his condition is deteriorating?

1. His radial pulse ranges from 76–80 beats/min.
2. He reports that his headache persists. *headache increases as deterioration from head injury*
3. The power of his right hand grasp is weak. *muscle weakness increases as neurologic status decreases*
4. His pupils are large and reactive. *reactive pupils is sign of improving not deteriorating*

GO TO NEXT PAGE

87. Which one of the following actions by the practical nurse/nursing assistant is most appropriate when charting nursing interventions?
    1. Make clear and concise entries. *clear, concise, easily understood & legal document*
    2. Erase or white-out errors in the entries.
    3. Sign the day's entries at the end of the shift. *Signed c it's written*
    4. Write entries in pen or pencil. *∅ pencil*

88. Which one of the following interventions should the practical nurse/nursing assistant implement when assisting an elderly female client with a bed bath?
    1. Wash her eyes from the outer to the inner canthus. *microorganisms drawn into eyes*
    2. Give perineal care prior to washing her back. *given last*
    3. Use long and firm, but gentle strokes. *help stimulate circulation*
    4. Lather her feet and toes well. *aggravate already dry skin of the elderly client* *producing bubbles*

89. The practical nurse/nursing assistant is unclear about how to perform a particular procedure for a client. A description of the procedure is not found in the procedure manual. Which one of the following actions by the practical nurse/nursing assistant is most appropriate?
    1. Check with the client as to how the procedure was last done. *may not correct*
    2. Ask the nurse-in-charge to clarify the procedure.
    3. Carry out the procedure. *not performed c complete knowledge*
    4. Have another practical nurse/nursing assistant perform the procedure. *neglecting personal responsibil*

90. The cord on a bedside lamp of a hospitalized client has become frayed. Which one of the following interventions by the practical nurse/nursing assistant is most appropriate?
    1. Wrap the cord thoroughly with electrical tape. *Not role of PN*
    2. Remove the lamp for a check by the maintenance department. *eliminate hazards allow repairs*
    3. Allow the client to use the lamp, provided the plug is not touched. *electric shock st possible*
    4. Document the condition of the lamp on the client's chart. *does not rectify problem*

91. Mrs. Jones, 70 years old, has been receiving chemotherapy and has a tendency for bleeding gums. Which one of the following interventions should the practical nurse/nursing assistant initiate if Mrs. Jones' gums begin to bleed during oral care?
    1. Discontinue oral care and offer her ice chips. *allows clot to form* *vaso constrict*
    2. Wrap finger in saline-moistened gauze and clean her teeth. *unplored wound c bleeding*
    3. Have her rinse with hydrogen peroxide and apply an ice pack. *cause further complications*
    4. Position her in low-Fowler's and apply pressure with gauze. *blood run down the throat causing choking*

72

92. During morning care, Mrs. Duclos, 68 years old, becomes upset and tells the practical nurse/nursing assistant to leave her alone. Which one of the following responses should the practical nurse/nursing assistant make to encourage Mrs. Duclos to express her feelings?
    1. "I can't leave you alone yet, because I'm not finished with your bath." *expression feeling*
    2. "I only have a few more things to do, then I'll leave."
    3. "You seem upset. Can you tell me what is bothering you?" *state obvious / open*
    4. "You know, it's not good to be upset when you are sick." *giving advice*

93. Colin, 8 years old, has an oral temperature of 40.5° C. Which one of the following actions should the practical nurse/nursing assistant perform initially?
    1. Recheck the temperature in 30 minutes. *nurse in charge for further assessment/intervent*
    2. Begin a tepid sponge bath. *require Dr.'s order*
    3. Offer extra fluids to combat dehydration. *may be contradictory to health status*
    4. Report the finding to the nurse-in-charge. *first report finding for possible tx/intervent*

94. Which one of the following positions is most appropriate for a client using a bedpan?
    1. Supine *cause hyperextension of hip*
    2. Fowler's *normal position for elimination, prevent back strain*
    3. Sims' *buttock not in direct contact c bedpan*
    4. Dorsal recumbent *for pt c restricted back movt.*

95. Mrs. Wills, 70 years old, is presently receiving a blood transfusion. Which one of the following observations must the practical nurse/nursing assistant report and record immediately?
    1. Leg cramps *ø related to blood transfusion*
    2. Cool extremities
    3. Urticaria *allergic reaction for incompatibility of blood*
    4. Polyuria

96. Tara Legros, 17 years old, has been hospitalized for surgery to correct scoliosis. On her first postoperative day, Tara asks why she must do leg exercises every hour. Which one of the following responses by the practical nurse/nursing assistant is most appropriate?
    1. "The exercises will make you feel more energetic and improve your appetite."
    2. "The exercises will ensure good blood flow to your legs and help prevent blood clots." *facilitate circulation*
    3. "You will recover quickly from your surgery if you do your exercises."
    4. "The leg exercises are important to keep your heart strong and healthy."

97. Carl, 16 years old, has an infected, draining toenail. Which one of the following recordings by the practical nurse/nursing assistant who has changed the dressing on the toenail is most accurate? — not accurate, lack sufficient detail
    1. Small amount of yellow pus noted when dressing changed on right great toe.
    2. Moderate amount of yellow drainage on one 2x2 from the right side of toe
    3. Purulent yellow discharge on one 2x2; right side of toe, red, warm to touch = identify
    4. 1x1 cm area, medial side of right great toe, scant purulent discharge noted. which toe
       size   location   drainage

98. Susie, 7 years old, has insulin dependent (Type I) diabetes mellitus. Which one of the following manifestations should indicate to the practical nurse/nursing assistant that Susie is likely having a hypoglycemic reaction? = low blood sugar ~ insulin shock
    1. Warm dry skin, flushed cheeks, and sweet breath odor hyperglycemia
    2. Cool moist skin, flushed cheeks, and abdominal pain
    3. Cool clammy skin, pallor, and weakness
    4. Increased urinary output, increased thirst, and visual disturbances

99. Which one of the following manifestations should indicate to the practical nurse/nursing assistant that a recently circumcised male infant may have an infection?
    1. A yellowish white scab forms on the glans penis. granulat g process of yellow tiss
    2. Erythema spreads beyond the edges of the wound.
    3. The tympanic temperature is 37.5° C.   normal
    4. There is a smell of ammonia with diaper removal. decomposit? of urine → norm

100. A female client, 48 years old, reports a cold left foot and has mottled skin with no evidence of edema. Which one of the following interventions should the practical nurse/nursing assistant implement?
    1. Encourage ankle exercises. need assessment 1st.
    2. Elevate her left leg. Ø if arterial insufficiency
    3. Assess her dorsalis pedis pulse. ✓ assess circulation of foot
    4. Cover her with a blanket. 1st to detect impaired circulation
       ↓ = slight overall vasodilation,

101. The practical nurse/nursing assistant is asked to prepare Mr. Martin for his breakfast. Which one of the following interventions should the practical nurse/nursing assistant perform first?
    1. Prepare for oral hygiene.
    2. Allow Mr. Martin to wash his hands.
    3. Provide an opportunity for elimination. avoid interruptions by eliminat? need
    4. Position the overbed table.

74

102. Mr. Pearce, 68 years old, has just returned from abdominal surgery. Which one of the following interventions by the practical nurse/nursing assistant is most appropriate?
    1. Place him in a side-lying position to decrease his abdominal pain. *not ↓ pain*
    2. Ask him to demonstrate his ankle exercises. *done later*
    3. Have him begin deep breathing. *reexpand lung & eliminate anesthetic after surgery*
    4. Position him in high-Fowler's for lung expansion.
    will enhance pain in pt c̄ abdominal surgery

103. A 70-year-old client who requires a mechanical lift is scheduled to have a tub bath. Which one of the following activities should the practical nurse/nursing assistant initiate first after checking on the availability of the tub?
    1. Discuss the benefits of having a tub bath. *Not priority*
    2. Explain the procedure involved in having a tub bath. *not priority*
    3. Collaborate with the client about the bath. *pt's right to determine how bath is done*
    4. Tell the client the time the practical nurse/nursing assistant will be ready to give the bath. *pt's right is ignored*

END OF INDEPENDENT QUESTIONS

END OF BOOK 2

80 / 103

A9-9997

CANADIAN NURSES ASSOCIATION

TESTING DIVISION

PRACTICAL NURSE/NURSING ASSISTANT
REGISTRATION/LICENSURE EXAMINATION

CANDIDATE NUMBER

SIGNATURE

BOOK 3
TEST FORM 9998

READ THE INSTRUCTIONS AND SAMPLE QUESTION INSIDE THE FRONT COVER

CANADIAN NURSES ASSOCIATION
ASSOCIATION DES INFIRMIÈRES ET INFIRMIERS DU CANADA

INSTRUCTIONS

A) TESTING TIME AND MATERIAL

You will have 30 minutes to work on this test book. The starting and finishing times will be announced and you will be advised when there are 15 and 5 minutes working time remaining. If at any time you have any questions about what you should do, raise your hand and an invigilator will assist you.

You will be advised whether you may leave the examination room if you finish the test book before the time is up. You must **stop** working when the signal is given. An invigilator will check your test book and answer sheet **before** you leave.

Clear your desk of all materials except your identification card, answer sheet, test book, pencils, and eraser. **Do not** fold, bend, or tear your answer sheet, as this could affect the scoring of your test.

B) ANSWER SHEET

Write your name, date of birth, date of writing, and test title in the corresponding boxes. Enter in your CANDIDATE NUMBER, the WRITING CENTRE CODE, and the TEST FORM and fill in the corresponding ovals. If you do not have a candidate number leave this section blank. Complete the box labeled LANGUAGE OF WRITING.

Be sure the mark you make for each answer is black, fills the oval, and contains the number corresponding to the number of the answer you have chosen. Do **not** fill in more than one oval for a question or you will not get credit for it. Erase **completely** any answer you wish to change and mark your new choice in the correct oval. An incomplete erasure may be read incorrectly as an intended answer. Do not press too heavily on your pencil or you may damage the answer sheet.

Note that the questions on the answer sheet are numbered in columns. There are fewer questions in the test book than there are numbers on the answer sheet.

Make no stray marks on the answer sheet; they may count against you. You may use the margins of the test book for any scratch work, but you will **not** get credit for anything you write in the test book.

C) TEST BOOK

Sign your name on the line on the cover of this book and copy your candidate number into the appropriate boxes. If you do not have a candidate number, **print** your name under your signature.

Read each question carefully and choose the answer you think is **correct**. If you cannot decide on an answer to a question, go on to the next one and come back to this question later if you have time. Try to answer all questions. Marks are not subtracted for wrong answers. If you are not sure of an answer, it will be to your advantage to guess. It will probably be best to start at the beginning of the test book and work through the questions in order.

This examination contains a number of experimental questions being tested for future use. Your answers to these questions will **not** count toward your score. Because you will not be able to tell which questions are experimental, you should do your best on all questions, but do **not** spend too much time on any question.

The questions in the examination are single questions unrelated to one another. The context of some questions may seem similar to others in your test book. This reflects current practice where a practical nurse/nursing assistant may have to care for different clients with similar problems. Each question, however, tests different nursing content. The sample question on the next page shows the type of questions used. The correct answer is blackened in the ovals on the right.

SAMPLE QUESTION

1. How should the practical nurse/nursing assistant view and position the ear canal when administering ear drops to a 2-year-old client?

    1. Pull the pinna downward and straight back.
    2. Pull the ear lobe upward and back.
    3. Pull the pinna downward and forward.
    4. Pull the ear lobe downward.   ●②③④

DO NOT GO TO THE NEXT PAGE OR BEGIN WORKING
UNTIL THE SIGNAL IS GIVEN TO DO SO

short-term care to provide relief for family caregivers

1. Mr. Ng had a cerebrovascular accident 1 year ago and is admitted for respite care. He is to *CVA* continue taking warfarin sodium (Coumadin), digoxin (Lanoxin), furosemide (Lasix), and lorazepam (Ativan). Mr. Ng asks the practical nurse/nursing assistant to obtain an order for acetylsalicylic acid (Aspirin) because he has a terrible headache. Which one of the following rationales best explains why the practical nurse/nursing assistant cannot accommodate Mr. Ng's request?

   1. Acetylsalicylic acid and warfarin sodium have an increased anticoagulant effect.
   2. Acetylsalicylic acid and digoxin have an increased bradycardiac effect.
   3. Acetylsalicylic acid and furosemide have an increased diuretic effect.
   4. Acetylsalicylic acid and lorazepam have an increased sedative effect.

2. Mrs. White is prescribed a miconazole nitrate (Monistat) suppository. The practical *antifungals* nurse/nursing assistant gives the miconazole nitrate per rectum. Which of the following actions must the practical nurse/nursing assistant take immediately?
   1. Retrieve the suppository using sterile gloves. *might push a further up into rectum*
   2. Fill out an incident report and call the physician. *assess first*
   3. Notify the nurse-in-charge of the error. *assess for possible side effect of error*
   4. Inform Mrs. White of the error and ask her to void. *assess first*

3. Mr. Suri, 47 years old, has insulin dependent (Type I) diabetes mellitus. After the practical nurse/nursing assistant administers his insulin (Humulin) injection, Mr. Suri asks why the practical nurse/nursing assistant did not massage his skin after the injection. Which one of the following responses by the practical nurse/nursing assistant is most appropriate?

   1. "Our hospital policy does not allow us to massage after subcutaneous injections."
   2. "I am sorry, Mr. Suri, I wasn't quite finished yet. I will massage it for you now."
   3. "It depends on the health care worker administering the medication. Some feel that massage improves absorption."
   4. "We do not massage after insulin injections because it affects absorption." *unpredictable absorp. of medicat. irritat. to site*

4. Mr. Hall is in a palliative care unit and has been receiving morphine sulfate (Morphine) on a regular basis for the past month. Mr. Hall's family expresses a concern about addiction and requests that Mr. Hall's medication be changed. Which one of the following responses is most appropriate for the practical nurse/nursing assistant to make to the family?

   1. "Mr. Hall is addicted to morphine, but the priority for him right now is his comfort." *not appropriate*
   2. "Pain control, not addiction, is the priority for Mr. Hall, and this medication is relieving his pain effectively." *demonstrate knowledge of medicat. total care plan*
   3. "Our goal is to promote Mr. Hall's comfort and the enjoyment of his remaining days." *not address to concern: addition*
   4. "I will talk to the nurse-in-charge to see if Mr. Hall's analgesic can be reduced or changed." *not appropriate*

80

5. Mr. Macht has a feeding tube in place and receives his medication via this route. One of his medications is available only in pill form. Which one of the following factors is most important for the practical nurse/nursing assistant to consider before administering this medication?
    1. The amount of liquid needed to dissolve the pill *any amount ✓*
    2. How the action of the medication changes when the pill is crushed *absorption fm GI tract occurs rapidly*
    3. Mr. Macht's weight
    4. Mr. Macht's vital signs

6. Which one of the following classifications of cream is commonly applied to the rectum in the treatment of hemorrhoids?
    1. Antitussive *cough suppressant.*
    2. Anesthetic *relief of pain*
    3. Antiseptic
    4. Antipyretic

7. Betty Tinsdale has been ordered a vaginal cream for severe vaginitis. The practical nurse/nursing assistant inserts the cream t.i.d. Following insertion of the cream, what information, in addition to the name of the medication, is most important for the practical nurse/nursing assistant to document on the chart?
    1. How the client tolerated the procedure
    2. The assessment of the vaginal mucosa *require insertion of speculum*
    3. The position the client was placed in for administration of the cream *many factors to determine position*
    4. The use of medical aseptic technique when administering the cream *not required to document.*

8. Which one of the following descriptions best characterizes a narcotic analgesic?
    1. Its effects cannot be blocked by antagonists. *are blocked*
    2. It does not react with other central nervous system depressants. *interact*
    3. It usually produces a greater analgesic effect than non-narcotic analgesics. *even higher dosage of non-narcotic*
    4. It causes uniform depression throughout major brain structures. *not uniform depression, but c isolated membranes y brain and spinal cord*

9. Immediately following the administration of penicillin G (Megacillin) via a feeding tube, the client states that he had an allergic reaction to ampicillin (Penbritin) several years ago. No allergies are listed on his chart. Which of the following interventions are most appropriate for the practical nurse/nursing assistant to implement initially?
    1. Ask the client to list all of his allergies.
    2. Discuss with the client the differences between the two medications.
    3. Ask the client to describe the reaction he had several years ago. *help planning/treatment*
    4. Monitor the client's blood pressure and respirations. *1st important to know allergic response*

81

A9-9998 **GO TO NEXT PAGE**

10. Lindsay Park, 12 years old, has just been diagnosed with insulin dependent (Type I) diabetes mellitus, and requires teaching to administer her own insulin (Humulin). Lindsay's mother reveals that Lindsay has a fear of needles. Which one of the following strategies is most appropriate for the practical nurse/nursing assistant to implement to help Lindsay learn to administer her own insulin?

indefinitely delay essential learning

    1. Delay teaching until Lindsay has accepted her need for insulin injections.
    2. Focus on preparation of the syringe and dietary concerns.
    3. Arrange practice sessions to provide Lindsay with the opportunity to handle a syringe. *opportunity to express her fear*
    4. Instruct Lindsay's mother to administer the injections.

11. Mr. Ryan, 28 years old, received 15 units of insulin (Humulin) at 08 00 hours. Shortly after, the practical nurse/nursing assistant notices that Mr. Ryan's skin is cold and clammy, and he seems confused. Which of the following interventions should be the practical nurse's/nursing assistant's first priority?

more appropriate for hyperglycemic pt?

    1. Encourage Mr. Ryan to drink plenty of clear fluids, and notify the nurse-in-charge.
    2. Offer Mr. Ryan 45 mL (3 tablespoons) of sugar immediately, and notify the nurse-in-charge. *10 mL of sugar (2 teaspoon) is adequate*
    3. Give Mr. Ryan half a glass of pure fruit juice and measure his blood glucose. *fast acting*
    4. Call the I.V. nurse because Mr. Ryan may need I.V. glucose.

12. Mr. Bach is to receive medicated inhalation therapy via aerosol. Which one of the following actions should promote safety for the practical nurse/nursing assistant when assisting with the administration of this medication?

    1. Wear a paper mask when checking for the mist emitted.
    2. Wear gloves when handling the medication.
    3. Avoid inhaling any of the mist emitted. *avoid becoming medicated*
    4. Administer the medication using a venturi mask or an aerochamber.

mist or still in air   *not for liquid administ*

13. Mrs. Parsons, 83 years old, has chronic back pain and is immobile. She is taking an oral narcotic analgesic for her pain. Which of the following nursing interventions would be most beneficial for this client?

need order. not address to narcotics/immobility

    1. Apply heat to Mrs. Parsons' back to decrease her need for analgesics.
    2. Encourage Mrs. Parsons to take extra fluids, prune juice, and bran. *constipat is common side effect of*
    3. Arrange for Mrs. Parsons to have apple juice and a whole wheat muffin for a *narcotic* snack. *constipat effect*   *fibre than bran and prune juice*
    4. Caution Mrs. Parsons against dependency on the medication, and provide it when absolutely necessary.

pain med should not be withheld

82

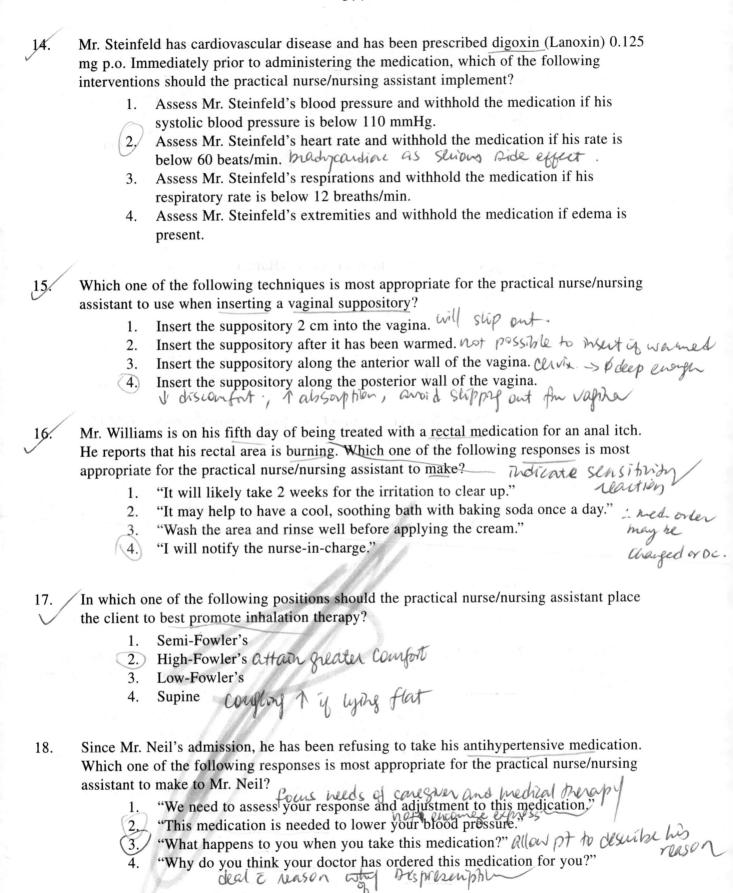

14. Mr. Steinfeld has cardiovascular disease and has been prescribed digoxin (Lanoxin) 0.125 mg p.o. Immediately prior to administering the medication, which of the following interventions should the practical nurse/nursing assistant implement?

 1. Assess Mr. Steinfeld's blood pressure and withhold the medication if his systolic blood pressure is below 110 mmHg.
 2. Assess Mr. Steinfeld's heart rate and withhold the medication if his rate is below 60 beats/min. *bradycardia as serious side effect.*
 3. Assess Mr. Steinfeld's respirations and withhold the medication if his respiratory rate is below 12 breaths/min.
 4. Assess Mr. Steinfeld's extremities and withhold the medication if edema is present.

15. Which one of the following techniques is most appropriate for the practical nurse/nursing assistant to use when inserting a vaginal suppository?

 1. Insert the suppository 2 cm into the vagina. *will slip out.*
 2. Insert the suppository after it has been warmed. *not possible to insert if warmed*
 3. Insert the suppository along the anterior wall of the vagina. *cervix → Ø deep enough*
 4. Insert the suppository along the posterior wall of the vagina. *↓ discomfort, ↑ absorption, avoid slipping out fm vagina*

16. Mr. Williams is on his fifth day of being treated with a rectal medication for an anal itch. He reports that his rectal area is burning. Which one of the following responses is most appropriate for the practical nurse/nursing assistant to make? *indicate sensitivity/ reaction*

 1. "It will likely take 2 weeks for the irritation to clear up."
 2. "It may help to have a cool, soothing bath with baking soda once a day." *∴ med. order may be*
 3. "Wash the area and rinse well before applying the cream." *changed or DC.*
 4. "I will notify the nurse-in-charge."

17. In which one of the following positions should the practical nurse/nursing assistant place the client to best promote inhalation therapy?

 1. Semi-Fowler's
 2. High-Fowler's *attain greater comfort*
 3. Low-Fowler's
 4. Supine *coughing ↑ if lying flat*

18. Since Mr. Neil's admission, he has been refusing to take his antihypertensive medication. Which one of the following responses is most appropriate for the practical nurse/nursing assistant to make to Mr. Neil?

 1. "We need to assess your response and adjustment to this medication." *focus needs of caregiver and medical therapy*
 2. "This medication is needed to lower your blood pressure." *not enhance express.*
 3. "What happens to you when you take this medication?" *allow pt to describe his reason*
 4. "Why do you think your doctor has ordered this medication for you?" *deal c reason why ∆ prescription*

83

GO TO NEXT PAGE

19. Which one of the following interventions is most important for the practical nurse/nursing assistant to implement to help prevent reinfection of the client who requires repeated intravaginal insertion of a cream?
    1. Instruct the client to remain supine for 5 to 10 minutes. *to facilitate melting of med only*
    2. Apply a perineal pad from front to back. *to prevent leakage*
    3. Remove gloves by turning them inside out. *to prevent cross infect⁼, not reinfec*
    4. Wash the applicator in hot soapy water. *After each use*

20. Which one of the following routes should the practical nurse/nursing assistant use when administering an ophthalmic suspension to a client?
    1. Oral
    2. Eye drop
    3. Nasal spray
    4. Inhalation

21. Mrs. Lee is receiving several oral medications, some of which are enteric-coated. Due to a recent cerebrovascular accident, she now has difficulty swallowing pills. Which of the following interventions are most appropriate for the practical nurse/nursing assistant to implement?
    1. Crush the pills and place them in jam. *destroy protective coat's → gastrointestinal irritat⁼*
    2. Report her difficulty swallowing pills to the nurse-in-charge. *may require med in another form*
    3. Dissolve the pills in water. *not likely*
    4. Administer the medications in their liquid form. *not the role of PN to change the form*

END OF BOOK 3

16/21

84

CANADIAN NURSES ASSOCIATION

TESTING DIVISION

PRACTICAL NURSE/NURSING ASSISTANT
REGISTRATION/LICENSURE EXAMINATION

CANDIDATE NUMBER

SIGNATURE

BOOK 4
TEST FORM 9999

READ THE INSTRUCTIONS AND SAMPLE QUESTION INSIDE THE FRONT COVER

CANADIAN NURSES ASSOCIATION
ASSOCIATION DES INFIRMIÈRES ET INFIRMIERS DU CANADA

INSTRUCTIONS

A) TESTING TIME AND MATERIAL

You will have 30 minutes to work on this test book. The starting and finishing times will be announced and you will be advised when there are 15 and 5 minutes working time remaining. If at any time you have any questions about what you should do, raise your hand and an invigilator will assist you.

You will be advised whether you may leave the examination room if you finish the test book before the time is up. You must **stop** working when the signal is given. An invigilator will check your test book and answer sheet **before** you leave.

Clear your desk of all materials except your identification card, answer sheet, test book, pencils, and eraser. **Do not** fold, bend, or tear your answer sheet, as this could affect the scoring of your test.

B) ANSWER SHEET

Write your name, date of birth, date of writing, and test title in the corresponding boxes. Enter in your CANDIDATE NUMBER, the WRITING CENTRE CODE, and the TEST FORM and fill in the corresponding ovals. If you do not have a candidate number leave this section blank. Complete the box labeled LANGUAGE OF WRITING.

Be sure the mark you make for each answer is black, fills the oval, and contains the number corresponding to the number of the answer you have chosen. Do **not** fill in more than one oval for a question or you will not get credit for it. Erase **completely** any answer you wish to change and mark your new choice in the correct oval. An incomplete erasure may be read incorrectly as an intended answer. Do not press too heavily on your pencil or you may damage the answer sheet.

Note that the questions on the answer sheet are numbered in columns. There are fewer questions in the test book than there are numbers on the answer sheet.

Make no stray marks on the answer sheet; they may count against you. You may use the margins of the test book for any scratch work, but you will **not** get credit for anything you write in the test book.

C) TEST BOOK

Sign your name on the line on the cover of this book and copy your candidate number into the appropriate boxes. If you do not have a candidate number, **print** your name under your signature.

Read each question carefully and choose the answer you think is **correct**. If you cannot decide on an answer to a question, go on to the next one and come back to this question later if you have time. Try to answer all questions. Marks are not subtracted for wrong answers. If you are not sure of an answer, it will be to your advantage to guess. It will probably be best to start at the beginning of the test book and work through the questions in order.

This examination contains a number of experimental questions being tested for future use. Your answers to these questions will **not** count toward your score. Because you will not be able to tell which questions are experimental, you should do your best on all questions, but do **not** spend too much time on any question.

The questions in the examination are single questions unrelated to one another. The context of some questions may seem similar to others in your test book. This reflects current practice where a practical nurse/nursing assistant may have to care for different clients with similar problems. Each question, however, tests different nursing content. The sample question on the next page shows the type of questions used. The correct answer is blackened in the ovals on the right.

86

SAMPLE QUESTION

1. When discontinuing an I.V. infusion, which one of the following interventions should the practical nurse/nursing assistant implement to protect the integrity of the client's vein?

    1. Apply pressure prior to removal of the needle/catheter.
    2. Remove the needle/catheter with an intermittent pulling action.
    3. Remove the needle/catheter with a steady pulling action.
    4. Apply a gauze dressing prior to removal of the needle/catheter.   ①②●④

DO NOT GO TO THE NEXT PAGE OR BEGIN WORKING
UNTIL THE SIGNAL IS GIVEN TO DO SO

1. A client is ambulating with an infusion control device in place. Which of the following elements of the I.V. infusion should the practical nurse/nursing assistant check first?
   1. Amount to be absorbed and rate of flow *managed by control device*
   2. Solution type and amount to be absorbed *these aren't managed by device.*
   3. Position for gravity and amount to be absorbed *irrelevant*
   4. Solution type and position for gravity

2. Which of the following types of antibodies in blood serum are characteristic of a client with type A blood?
   1. Anti-A
   2. Anti-B
   3. None *type AB has no antibodies*
   4. Anti-A and anti-B *type o.*

3. The practical nurse/nursing assistant is obtaining albumin from the blood bank. The practical nurse/nursing assistant should be aware that this blood product is best for a client with which one of the following conditions?
   1. Deficiency of plasma protein
   2. Multiple coagulation deficiencies *adm plasma*
   3. Severely low hemoglobin *whole blood and packed cells*
   4. Deficiency of platelets *adm. platelets*

4. The nurse-in-charge has asked the practical nurse/nursing assistant to prepare 1,000 mL of D5W as an I.V. solution for a client. Which one of the following interventions should the practical nurse/nursing assistant implement first?
   1. Wash hands using medical aseptic technique.
   2. Prepare the equipment and the I.V. solution.
   3. Inform the client that an I.V. solution is to be administered.
   4. Check the physician's order to confirm the solution to prepare.

5. While caring for a client with an I.V. infusion, which is ordered to run at 125 mL/h, the practical nurse/nursing assistant observes that there are 100 mL remaining in the solution bag. Which one of the following interventions should the practical nurse/nursing assistant implement first?
   1. Slow the infusion rate.
   2. Check the physician's order. *determine need for further IV solut^n*
   3. Obtain a new bag of solution. *&*
   4. Assess the infusion site.

88

6. The practical nurse/nursing assistant has returned to the unit with a blood product ordered for a client. The nurse-in-charge is off the unit and a registered nurse is working with a critically ill client. How should the practical nurse/nursing assistant proceed?
   1. Ask another practical nurse/nursing assistant to verify and co-sign the requisition.
   2. Wait until the registered nurse is finished with the critically ill client.
   3. Notify the registered nurse that the blood product is ready to be checked.
   4. Page the nurse-in-charge to co-sign the requisition.

7. When the practical nurse/nursing assistant is discontinuing an I.V. infusion, which one of the following actions is most important as a means of ensuring client safety?
   1. Dispose of equipment using universal precautions.
   2. Apply pressure to the site to prevent bleeding.
   3. Use double gloves throughout the procedure.
   4. Clamp the tubing before beginning.

8. A client has been admitted for treatment of dehydration. An I.V. infusion has been ordered to infuse at 125 mL/h through macrodrip tubing which has a drip factor of 15 gtt/mL. The practical nurse/nursing assistant enters the client's room and notes that the I.V. infusion is running at 25 gtt/min. Which of the following interventions should the practical nurse/nursing assistant implement?
   1. Maintain the present drop rate.
   2. Decrease the drop rate to 17 gtt/min.
   3. Increase the drop rate to 31 gtt/min.
   4. Increase the drop rate to 56 gtt/min.

9. The practical nurse/nursing assistant goes to the blood bank to pick up packed cells and receives whole blood labeled with the client data. Which of the following actions is most appropriate for the practical nurse/nursing assistant to take next?
   1. Question the lab about the accuracy of the product received with the product ordered.
   2. Return to the nursing unit with the product.
   3. Proceed with the blood administration at the bedside.
   4. Do the second safety check with a registered nurse at the nursing station.

10. Which one of the following procedures by the practical nurse/nursing assistant is most appropriate to accurately identify a client who is to receive a blood transfusion?
   1. Check the client's identification band with the physician's order.
   2. Check the client's identification band and ask the client to state own name.
   3. Call the client by name and check the identification band.
   4. Ask the nurse-in-charge and check the identification band.

GO TO NEXT PAGE

11. The practical nurse/nursing assistant is preparing a client with an I.V. infusion for ambulation with a portable I.V. pole. Which one of the following directions should be given to the client?
    1. Keep the affected limb near the waist. *can maintain the flow rate*
    2. Keep the affected limb elevated. *↓ flow rate*
    3. Raise the pole as the fluid level of the bag lowers. *↑ flow rate*
    4. Lower the pole as the fluid level of the bag lowers. *height of pole not altered*

12. When setting up an I.V. infusion for a pediatric client, which one of the following infusion sets should be obtained by the practical nurse/nursing assistant?
    1. A macrodrip set delivering 10 gtt/mL.
    2. A macrodrip set delivering 60 gtt/mL.
    3. A microdrip set delivering 10 gtt/mL.
    4. A microdrip set delivering 60 gtt/mL. *Small dosage + volume for paediatric pts.*

13. While discontinuing an I.V. infusion, the practical nurse/nursing assistant notes fluid leaking at the site. Which one of the following interventions is most appropriate for the practical nurse/nursing assistant to implement?
    1. Check the site for infiltration. *check during the infusion*
    2. Inspect the tubing for breaks.
    3. Assess the needle/catheter/tubing joint for leakage.
    4. Ensure the tubing roller clamp is turned off. *check c̄ d/c infusion*

14. The practical nurse/nursing assistant is monitoring an I.V. infusion of blood. Which one of the following factors is most important for the practical nurse/nursing assistant to consider for rate of flow?
    1. Condition of the tubing *Can be a factor if kinky, not most important*
    2. Color of the infusion site *not.*
    3. Viscosity of the solution *directly affect rate of flow*
    4. Length of I.V. tubing *not relevant.*

15. When changing an I.V. solution container, which of the following data should be included in documentation by the practical nurse/nursing assistant?
    1. Time, total I.V. intake, volume infused *& type of solution*
    2. Volume infused, type of solution, total I.V. intake *not a consideration.*
    3. Total I.V. intake, type of solution, time
    4. Type of solution, time, volume infused

A9-9999

16. Mrs. Smith, 80 years old, is receiving I.V. therapy. The practical nurse/nursing assistant enters Mrs. Smith's room and notes that the rate of flow has increased. Which one of the following interventions should the practical nurse/nursing assistant perform first?
    1. Check the rate of the I.V. infusion. *essential to determine rate.*
    2. Check to ensure that the tubing is not kinked.
    3. Encourage Mrs. Smith not to touch the I.V. clamp.
    4. Provide Mrs. Smith with instructions about the I.V. infusion.

17. Which one of the following reasons best supports the use of microdrip tubing?
    1. To maintain a rapid rate of infusion *macrodrip*
    2. To avoid infiltration of the solution *infiltration & tube size*
    3. To administer solutions to a dehydrated client
    4. To regulate precise rate of flow *for small & precise volume administer fluid slowly*

18. When co-signing for blood administration, it is necessary for the practical nurse/nursing assistant to be aware of which of the following data?
    1. The client's hemoglobin report
    2. The client's blood group and Rh factor
    3. The client's blood group and red cell count
    4. The client's Rh factor and red cell count

19. Which one of the following actions is the first responsibility of the practical nurse/nursing assistant in the management of an I.V. infusion immediately after the tubing has been changed?
    1. Assessing the I.V. site for signs of infiltration *routine assessment*
    2. Checking the solution volume remaining in the bag
    3. Assessing the patency of the tubing *not start until flow starts.*
    4. Regulating the flow of the infusion *ensure it runs*

20. When changing an I.V. bottle/bag, why is it important for the practical nurse/nursing assistant to prevent air from entering the tubing?
    1. Air in the tubing can increase the rate of flow of the infusion.
    2. Air in the tubing could cause an embolus.
    3. Air in the tubing can decrease the rate of flow of the infusion.
    4. Air in the tubing could cause a thrombus.

END OF BOOK 4

$\frac{14}{20}$

A9-9999

CHAPTER 5
Scoring the Practice Exam

This chapter outlines how to score each component of your Practice Exam. It describes how to calculate your score using the scoring key and how to interpret your result. It also describes how the actual PN/NA Exam is scored.

CALCULATING YOUR SCORE

Follow these steps to calculate your total raw score on the Practice Exam:

1. Go to the answer keys for the Practice Exam (see pages 97, 98 and 99). There is one key for each examination book.

2. Compare each of your responses to the correct answers given in the answer key. (Identify the questions you answered incorrectly by circling or highlighting them on your answer sheet, or by listing them on a separate sheet of paper. This will make it easier for you to create your Performance Profile, an exercise that is explained in the next chapter.)

3. Score one point for each correct answer. Score zero points for incorrect or blank answers. For "double responses" (i.e., where you selected more than one answer to a single question) you also score zero points, even if one of your answers is correct.

4. Use the following chart to record your score for each examination book and each component. Then for the Core Component, add together the scores for Books 1 and 2 to get the total Core Component raw score.

NUMBER OF QUESTIONS ANSWERED CORRECTLY

CORE COMPONENT

BOOK 1 _____/103
BOOK 2 _____/103
SUM OF BOOKS 1+ 2 _____/206
(this is the Core Component raw score)

MEDICATIONS COMPONENT

BOOK 3 _____/21
(this is the Medications Component raw score)

INTRAVENOUS/INFUSION THERAPY COMPONENT

BOOK 4 _____/20
(this is the Intravenous/Infusion Therapy Component raw score)

5. (a) Core Component: You can convert your total Core Component raw score into a percentage score by using the following formula:

PERCENTAGE SCORE

$$\frac{\text{TOTAL}}{206} \text{ (Core Component)} \quad \text{RAW SCORE} \quad \text{x} \quad 100 \quad = \quad \underline{\hspace{1cm}} \%$$

(b) Core and Medications Components: If you wrote the Medications Component of the Practice Exam, add your Medications Component raw score to your total Core Component raw score. You can convert this total raw score to a percentage score by using the following formula:

PERCENTAGE SCORE

$$\frac{\text{TOTAL}}{227} \text{ (Core + Medications)} \quad \text{RAW SCORE} \quad \text{x} \quad 100 \quad = \quad \underline{\hspace{1cm}} \%$$

(c) Core, Medications, and Intravenous/Infusion Therapy Components: If you wrote all three components of the Practice Exam, total the raw scores of the three components. You can convert this total raw score into a percentage score by using the following formula:

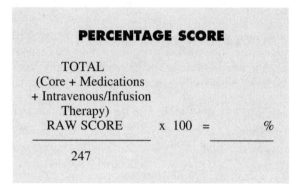

PERCENTAGE SCORE

TOTAL
(Core + Medications
+ Intravenous/Infusion
Therapy)
RAW SCORE   x 100 =   %

247

INTERPRETING YOUR SCORES

Although the total raw scores and percentage scores that you calculate are of a different type than the result you would receive on the actual PN/NA Exam (see next section, "How the Actual PN/NA Exam Is Scored"), they can provide useful feedback on your performance. Use the Score Interpretation Scale on page 96 for a quick assessment of your performance on the Practice Exam. The scale also outlines follow-up steps you can take to enhance your preparation for the PN/NA Exam. Note that no specific pass mark is set for the Practice Exam.

HOW THE ACTUAL PN/NA EXAM IS SCORED*

The PN/NA Exam is computer scored by CNAT. Only answers that are recorded on your answer sheets are scanned and scored. You do not receive any credit for questions that you answered only in the examination books and not on the answer sheets. Likewise, no credit is given where you selected more than one answer to a single question. It is essential that you read and follow the instructions inside each examination book on how to correctly mark your selected answers; otherwise, your score may be adversely affected.

After your answer sheets are scanned, the computer calculates your score on the examination. Your "pass" or "fail" result is determined by comparing this score to the established standard (pass mark).

The standard to be met on the PN/NA Exam is established before the examination is given. The standard is set by considering the content and difficulty of the test questions.

The standard-setting procedure used by CNAT involves panels of subject matter experts from across Canada. These subject matter experts are people who work closely with practical nurses/nursing assistants beginning to practice; they include educators, practical nurses/nursing assistants, and administrators. Their task is to determine a point on a measurement scale that represents the expected performance of a minimally competent practical nurse/nursing assistant beginning to practice. The experts are provided with extensive orientation and training by CNAT staff to ensure that they produce ratings based on the same understanding of the minimally competent beginning practitioner.

In addition to the expert ratings, a variety of relevant information is carefully considered to ensure that the standard is valid and fair. This can include information on the preparation of new graduates, data on the performance of candidates on previous examinations, and pertinent psychometric research findings. Based on all of this information, a point is set on a measurement scale that represents the minimum acceptable standard.

Because there are different versions of the examination, a candidate's score is converted to a common measurement scale and compared to the established passing point on that scale. Although different forms of the examination contain different sets of questions, this conversion ensures that all candidates are treated fairly and are evaluated against the same standard. If a candidate's score on this common scale is at or higher than the passing point, a pass result is achieved on the examination; if the score is lower than the passing point, a fail result is obtained.

The pass or fail result on the PN/NA Exam is reported on a Candidate Examination Report that is sent to candidates by their provincial or territorial registering/licensing authority. Candidates who fail the PN/NA Exam are also provided with feedback on their test performance. This feedback is similar to the information you can obtain by creating your Performance Profile (see Chapter 6).

* Based on the information available at the time of publication.

SCORE INTERPRETATION SCALE

RAW SCORE			PERFORMANCE INTERPRETATION	SUGGESTIONS FOR FOLLOW-UP

CORE, MEDICATIONS, & INTRAVENOUS/ INFUSION THERAPY | CORE & MEDICATIONS | CORE COMPONENT

STRONG

Review the rationales of the questions you answered incorrectly. The closer your score is to the borderline zone, the more you should consult the relevant texts that are cited. As well, by creating your Performance Profile (see Chapter 6), you may identify specific areas on which you should focus during your remaining preparation time. Before writing the PN/NA Exam, take another look at the Practice Exam questions that you answered incorrectly.

220 / 205 / 190

165 / 150 / 140

BORDERLINE

Create your Performance Profile to determine your areas of strength and weakness, and follow the strategies provided for dealing with your weaknesses (see Chapter 6). Review some general nursing textbooks, concentrating on the problem areas, and also consult textbooks specific to the problem areas. After your review, retake the Practice Exam before writing the actual PN/NA Exam.

125 / 115 / 105

110 / 100 / 90

WEAK

Create your Performance Profile (see Chapter 6) to gain a better understanding of your areas of weakness in the competency categories. In addition to reviewing some key nursing textbooks, be sure to read the rationales for all the questions in the Practice Exam. You may also benefit from reviewing the test-taking strategies in Chapter 3. Finally, retake the Practice Exam before taking the actual PN/NA Exam.

ANSWER KEY – BOOK 1
(CORE COMPONENT)

QUESTION NUMBER	CORRECT ANSWER
1.	4
2.	2
3.	2
4.	2
5.	3
6.	2
7.	2
8.	1
9.	1
10.	2
11.	3
12.	4
13.	1
14.	1
15.	1
16.	3
17.	2
18.	4
19.	2
20.	3
21.	1
22.	4
23.	2
24.	4
25.	2
26.	1

QUESTION NUMBER	CORRECT ANSWER
27.	1
28.	2
29.	2
30.	4
31.	3
32.	4
33.	1
34.	2
35.	1
36.	1
37.	3
38.	4
39.	1
40.	1
41.	1
42.	1
43.	1
44.	2
45.	3
46.	2
47.	4
48.	3
49.	3
50.	2
51.	3
52.	4

QUESTION NUMBER	CORRECT ANSWER
53.	3
54.	3
55.	3
56.	1
57.	4
58.	2
59.	3
60.	4
61.	3
62.	1
63.	2
64.	3
65.	4
66.	4
67.	4
68.	1
69.	1
70.	4
71.	1
72.	1
73.	1
74.	1
75.	3
76.	2
77.	1
78.	2

QUESTION NUMBER	CORRECT ANSWER
79.	1
80.	2
81.	3
82.	2
83.	1
84.	3
85.	3
86.	4
87.	3
88.	1
89.	3
90.	1
91.	1
92.	4
93.	3
94.	2
95.	4
96.	1
97.	4
98.	4
99.	2
100.	3
101.	4
102.	2
103.	3

ANSWER KEY – BOOK 2
(CORE COMPONENT)

QUESTION NUMBER	CORRECT ANSWER
1.	3
2.	2
3.	3
4.	4
5.	1
6.	1
7.	4
8.	3
9.	2
10.	4
11.	4
12.	3
13.	4
14.	3
15.	2
16.	1
17.	1
18.	3
19.	3
20.	1
21.	1
22.	1
23.	4
24.	4
25.	1
26.	3

QUESTION NUMBER	CORRECT ANSWER
27.	2
28.	1
29.	3
30.	1
31.	1
32.	4
33.	1
34.	2
35.	3
36.	4
37.	3
38.	4
39.	4
40.	4
41.	1
42.	1
43.	2
44.	1
45.	3
46.	2
47.	3
48.	4
49.	3
50.	1
51.	3
52.	4

QUESTION NUMBER	CORRECT ANSWER
53.	2
54.	4
55.	3
56.	1
57.	3
58.	2
59.	4
60.	1
61.	2
62.	1
63.	1
64.	2
65.	2
66.	4
67.	4
68.	1
69.	1
70.	2
71.	2
72.	2
73.	1
74.	4
75.	2
76.	2
77.	2
78.	4

QUESTION NUMBER	CORRECT ANSWER
79.	4
80.	2
81.	1
82.	3
83.	3
84.	4
85.	4
86.	3
87.	1
88.	3
89.	2
90.	2
91.	1
92.	3
93.	4
94.	2
95.	3
96.	2
97.	4
98.	3
99.	2
100.	3
101.	3
102.	3
103.	3

ANSWER KEY - BOOK 3
(MEDICATIONS COMPONENT)

QUESTION NUMBER	CORRECT ANSWER
1.	1
2.	3
3.	4
4.	2
5.	2
6.	2

QUESTION NUMBER	CORRECT ANSWER
7.	1
8.	3
9.	3
10.	3
11.	3
12.	3

QUESTION NUMBER	CORRECT ANSWER
13.	2
14.	2
15.	4
16.	4
17.	2
18.	3

QUESTION NUMBER	CORRECT ANSWER
19.	4
20.	2
21.	2

ANSWER KEY - BOOK 4
(INTRAVENOUS/INFUSION THERAPY COMPONENT)

QUESTION NUMBER	CORRECT ANSWER
1.	2
2.	2
3.	1
4.	4
5.	2
6.	3

QUESTION NUMBER	CORRECT ANSWER
7.	2
8.	3
9.	1
10.	2
11.	1
12.	4

QUESTION NUMBER	CORRECT ANSWER
13.	4
14.	3
15.	4
16.	1
17.	4
18.	2

QUESTION NUMBER	CORRECT ANSWER
19.	4
20.	2

CHAPTER 6
Creating Your Performance Profile

Once you have completed and scored the Practice Exam, you can create a personal Performance Profile that identifies your areas of strength and weakness on the examination, based on the Competency Categories. You need your scored answer sheets (or a list of the questions you answered incorrectly), a calculator, and the Performance Profile Tally Sheet and Performance Profile Chart (these are at the end of the *Prep Guide* and are perforated for easy removal).

CLASSIFICATION OF QUESTIONS

Each question in the Practice Exam has been classified within three different classification schemes: Competency Category, Taxonomic Level, and Client Age Group. Each question's classifications are indicated beside the question's rationales in Chapter 7. (The classification schemes are weighted elements from the *Blueprint*; see Chapter 2.)

The Competency Categories are used to create your Performance Profile. These categories are as follows:

Client Care – Assessment

Client Care – Planning

Client Care – Implementation

Client Care – Evaluation

Communication Skills

Professional and Personal Responsibilities

STEPS FOR CREATING YOUR PERFORMANCE PROFILE

The previous chapter, "Scoring the Practice Exam," asked you to identify on your answer sheets (or on a separate sheet) the questions you **answered incorrectly**. Now, by following steps 1 through 4, you can create your own Performance Profile.

1. On the **Performance Profile Tally Sheet**, for each question you answered incorrectly, place a mark in the row that corresponds to the Competency Category for that question (see Sample – Step 1). Only fill in the Tally Sheet for those components of the Practice Exam that you completed.

SAMPLE — STEP 1
PERFORMANCE PROFILE TALLY SHEET

COMPETENCY CATEGORY		TOTAL INCORRECT	% INCORRECT
CLIENT CARE			
• Assessment	~~HHH~~	÷ 51 X 100 =	%
• Planning	//	÷ 6 X 100 =	%
• Implementation			
– Core Component only	~~HHH~~ ///	÷ 102 X 100 –	

2. Total the marks in each row to determine the number of questions you answered incorrectly in each category. Record that number in the first shaded box in the row.

3. Calculate the percentage of questions you answered incorrectly for each category by doing the math at the end of each row (see Sample–Steps 2 & 3). (The percentage equals the number of questions you answered incorrectly divided by the total number of questions for that category and multiplied by 100.)

SAMPLE — STEPS 2 & 3
PERFORMANCE PROFILE TALLY SHEET

COMPETENCY CATEGORY	TOTAL INCORRECT	% INCORRECT
CLIENT CARE		
• Assessment *////*	**5** ÷ 51 X 100 =	**10** %
• Planning *//*	**2** ÷ 6 X 100 =	**33** %
• Implementation		
– *Core Component only* *//// ///*	**8** ÷ 102 X 100	

4. Create your **Performance Profile** by taking the percentage values from each category and darkening up to the corresponding level of the category rows on the Performance Profile Chart (see Sample — Step 4).

SAMPLE — STEP 4
PERFORMANCE PROFILE CHART

COMPETENCY CATEGORY

% OF INCORRECT ANSWERS	0	5	10	15	20	25	30	35	40	45	50	55	60

CLIENT CARE

   • Assessment

   • Planning

   • Implementation*

   • Evaluation

COMMUNICATION SKILLS

INTERPRETATION OF PERFORMANCE

The goal in creating your Performance Profile is to identify your areas of relative strength and weakness. This information can help you make the best use of your remaining preparation time. Generally, those Competency Categories in which you selected a high percentage of incorrect answers are the areas you should focus on during studying. However, this approach can be refined to allow you to make even better use of your time.

In looking at the TOTAL column on the Tally Sheet, you will notice that the number of questions in each category varies; some areas have relatively few questions whereas others have many. This is an important aspect of understanding your performance. Both the *percentage* of incorrect answers in a category and the *total number* of incorrect answers in a category should be carefully considered.

You will recall that the Competency Category is a weighted element of the examination *Blueprint*. This means that the number of questions in each competency category is different. By category, the distribution of questions in the Core Component of the Practice Exam, for example, is as follows:

Client Care – Assessment   51 questions

Client Care – Planning   6 questions

Client Care – Implementation   102 questions

Client Care – Evaluation   2 questions

Communication Skills   28 questions

Professional and Personal
    Responsibilities   17 questions

As well, the Medications Component has 21 questions, and the Intravenous/Infusion Therapy Component has 20 questions.

The following example illustrates the importance of considering both the percentage and the number of incorrect answers in a category. If your Performance Profile Chart shows that you selected the highest percentage of incorrect answers in the "Planning" category, you should keep in mind that a relatively small number of questions on the Core Component of the examination deal with Planning (i.e., 6 questions out of the total of 206). Even if you selected only correct answers for that category, the impact on your total score would be small. On the other hand, even a fairly low percentage of incorrect responses in the "Implementation" category (with as many as 102 questions out of the total of 206) can represent many questions on the examination. Consequently, improving your performance in this category by only a few percentage marks can make a greater difference overall.

Therefore, even though a high percentage of incorrect answers in a Competency Category indicates weakness in that category, your best strategy for studying may require you to focus on another category, one that has a greater representation on the examination.

Once you have determined which Competency Categories you need to improve in, you may wish to follow the three steps below:

1. Go to Appendix A and review the competencies in the categories identified as areas of weakness for you; this will give you an overview of the competencies that require your attention.

2. Review the questions that are classified in the competency categories you have identified as weaker for you. Include in your review both the questions you answered correctly and those you answered incorrectly; this will give you a more complete review of the content that measures the competencies you need to work on. Read the rationales for the correct and incorrect responses to get a better understanding of your areas of weakness.

3. Look up the references cited (or other comparable references) for the questions you answered incorrectly; this can increase your understanding of material you may not yet have fully mastered.

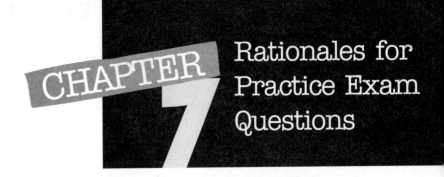

Chapter 7 presents detailed information on the Practice Exam questions. For each question, the following information is given:

- Correct Answer
- Rationales
- Competency Category
- Taxonomic Level
- Client Age Group
- References

Rationales provide an explanation of why the correct response is correct, and why the remaining options are incorrect. The information presented in each rationale relates directly to the corresponding option for that question. Reviewing the rationales of those questions you answered incorrectly may help you in your preparation for the actual PN/NA Exam.

Each question's correct answer is indicated next to the question number. Each question in the Practice Exam has been classified within three different classification schemes: Competency Category, Taxonomic Level, and Client Age Group (see Chapter 2 for explanations of these classifications). Each question's classifications are indicated beside the question's rationales. The Competency Category will be used to create your Performance Profile (see Chapter 6). The two references listed were used to create the question (see the Bibliography for the full citations). These references, among others, can be useful in achieving a more complete understanding of the reasons why the correct answer is correct and why the incorrect options are incorrect.

An example of the rationales and classification information is provided below.

RATIONALE EXAMPLE

103 CORRECT ANSWER: 3

1. Libel is a written statement that conveys an unfavorable impression.
2. This situation describes a breach of ethics as it deals with moral behavior. However, breach of confidentiality is a more specific term to use.
3. Breach of confidentiality is the violation of another person's right to privacy and is one type of nonethical behavior.
4. Verbal assault is a deliberate attempt to hurt another person. The health care workers did not necessarily mean to harm the client or his character.

CLASSIFICATION

Competency Category:	Professional and Personal Responsibilities
Taxonomic Level:	Knowledge/Comprehension
Client Age:	General

REFERENCES
Potter & Perry (1993), p. 281
Wilson & Kneisl (1992), p. 123

CASE 1

1 CORRECT ANSWER: 4

1. A mask is not required with enteric precautions.
2. Only individuals handling soiled materials need to wear a gown and gloves with enteric precautions.
3. The client may leave her room as long as she does not contaminate any furniture or utensils. She must use her own bathroom and practice good handwashing.
4. Enteric precautions prevent the spread of microorganisms by limiting contact with fecal materials; a gown and gloves would limit this contact.

CLASSIFICATION

Competency Category:	Client Care – Implementation
Taxonomic Level:	Application
Client Age:	Child & Adolescent

REFERENCES
Scherer (1991), p. 77
Smeltzer & Bare (1992), p. 1901

2 CORRECT ANSWER: 2

1. A dry container does not contain the medium that would preserve the ova and parasites until lab tests could be completed.
2. Stool specimens for ova and parasites must be collected in a container that contains a medium that preserves the ova and parasites.
3. A sterile container is not required for the collection of ova and parasites. Also, a sterile container does not contain the medium that would preserve the ova and parasites until lab tests could be completed.
4. A bulk stool specimen is required for testing of ova and parasites; a swab is not the correct procedure.

CLASSIFICATION

Competency Category:	Client Care – Implementation
Taxonomic Level:	Application
Client Age:	Child & Adolescent

REFERENCES
Taylor et al. (1993), pp. 907–908
Timby & Lewis (1992), pp. 566–567

3 CORRECT ANSWER: 2

1. This approach does not foster the client's participation in her care plan. As well, it is inappropriate to inform the client about an outcome that is not absolute.
2. Allowing the client to perform activities that she is capable of doing, such as intake and output, will foster her participation in the care plan.
3. This approach may be perceived by the client as controlling and will not likely foster client participation.
4. This approach may be perceived by the client as controlling and subsequently may result in further noncompliance with the care plan.

CLASSIFICATION

Competency Category:	Communication Skills
Taxonomic Level:	Application
Client Age:	Child & Adolescent

REFERENCES

Jackson & Saunders (1993), pp. 528–529
Whaley & Wong (1993), p. 458

4 CORRECT ANSWER: 2

1. Asking the client if she has enough cream left reflects the assessment phase of the nursing process.
2. Asking the client how the area around her rectum feels and observing it reflects the evaluation phase of the nursing process. Both subjective and objective data can validate that a goal has been reached.
3. Asking the client if care can be provided reflects the implementation phase of the nursing process.
4. Reminding the client to perform self–care reflects the implementation phase of the nursing process.

CLASSIFICATION

Competency Category:	Client Care – Evaluation
Taxonomic Level:	Application
Client Age:	Child & Adolescent

REFERENCES

Taylor et al. (1993), pp. 222–224
Timby & Lewis (1992), pp. 49–51

CORRECT ANSWER: 3

1. A common shower is incompatible with enteric precautions as it could become contaminated with fecal matter.
2. The physical environment would not likely allow the use of a stretcher in this manner.
3. Assisting the client while she sits at the sink is most appropriate because it is the least tiring activity for her and it satisfies her need for clean hair.
4. Having clean hair is very important to the well-being of an adolescent, especially when peers are coming to visit. Styling her hair does not meet the client's need to have clean hair.

CLASSIFICATION

Competency Category: Client Care – Implementation
Taxonomic Level: Application
Client Age: Child & Adolescent

REFERENCES

Taylor et al. (1993), pp. 618–619
Timby & Lewis (1992), p. 117

CORRECT ANSWER: 2

1. The middle adolescent is trying to separate emotionally from parents, so frequent visits would not help her with this task.
2. Friends are the most important aspects of an adolescent's life. Peers help them to develop socially and to separate emotionally from parents.
3. Although she is feeling better, she may still be infectious, especially to young children. Peers are the best recreational source for an adolescent.
4. Homework may not be a very attractive alternative to the adolescent. As well, having friends drop off the work is more isolating than having them visit.

CLASSIFICATION

Competency Category: Client Care – Implementation
Taxonomic Level: Application
Client Age: Child & Adolescent

REFERENCES

Thompson (1990), p. 478
Whaley & Wong (1993), p. 452

CASE 2

7 CORRECT ANSWER: 2

1. Sero-sanguineous drainage can indicate impending infection, but generally only with other signs present, such as inflamed skin edges. These edges, however, are nonirritated.
2. Inflamed skin edges combined with serous drainage are indicative of infection, and must be reported immediately.
3. Puffy skin edges may indicate impending infection, but without drainage it would be most appropriate to observe the site and report the findings at a later time.
4. Dried drainage indicates pin site care is needed, but with pink edges the sites are unlikely to be infected and need not be reported immediately.

CLASSIFICATION

Competency Category:	Client Care – Assessment
Taxonomic Level:	Critical Thinking
Client Age:	Adult

REFERENCES

Kozier et al. (1991), p. 455
Taylor et al. (1993), p. 1268

8 CORRECT ANSWER: 1

1. In skeletal traction, clients often lean on their elbows to change position. The protectors prevent friction of the elbows rubbing on the bedclothes, which can result in skin breakdown.
2. Any circumferential structure such as elbow protectors may cause, rather than prevent, constriction of blood vessels.
3. Any circumferential structure such as elbow protectors may cause, rather than lower, pressure on a nerve, resulting in damage.
4. Sheepskin will likely absorb the moisture, thus preventing skin breakdown.

CLASSIFICATION

Competency Category:	Client Care – Implementation
Taxonomic Level:	Critical Thinking
Client Age:	Adult

REFERENCES

Kozier et al. (1991), p. 876
Timby & Lewis (1992), p. 698

9 CORRECT ANSWER: 1

1. By tightening the muscles of his affected leg, the client will maintain muscle mass and strength without involving the joint.
2. The client should have no limitation in movement or loss of strength in his upper limbs and should be encouraged to do active range-of-motion to his upper limbs.
3. Although deep breathing and coughing exercises are beneficial, they will not maintain the client's muscle strength.
4. Because the client is in skeletal traction, he is unable to perform isotonic exercises that move his affected leg.

↳ active exercise, muscle contracts to cause movt.

greatly enhance joint mobility and help improve muscle strength/tone.
i.e. rise on tiptoes; stretching arms overhead

CLASSIFICATION

Competency Category:	Client Care – Implementation
Taxonomic Level:	Application
Client Age:	Adult

REFERENCES

Kozier et al. (1991), p. 879
Rosdahl (1991), p. 745

10 CORRECT ANSWER: 2

1. To roll laterally would change the line of pull and is contraindicated for the client in traction.
2. Lifting up with the aid of a trapeze would maintain the line of pull while the practical nurse/nursing assistant is making the bed.
3. In order to use the side rails, the client would have to roll, thereby changing the line of pull, which is contraindicated when in traction.
4. Having the client slide toward the foot of the bed would alter the angle of the traction and is contraindicated for the client in traction.

CLASSIFICATION

Competency Category:	Client Care – Implementation
Taxonomic Level:	Application
Client Age:	Adult

REFERENCES

Perry & Potter (1994), pp. 851–862
Timby & Lewis (1992), pp. 697–698

11 CORRECT ANSWER: 3

1. Areas that are constantly red should not be rubbed, with or without cream, as it may cause further tissue damage.
2. Areas that are constantly red should not be massaged with alcohol, as it may cause further tissue damage.
3. The red areas may be showing initial signs of tissue breakdown, and massage of these areas would cause further tissue damage.
4. Areas that are red should not have alcohol applied to them, as it may cause further tissue damage.

CLASSIFICATION

Competency Category:	Client Care – Implementation
Taxonomic Level:	Application
Client Age:	Adult

REFERENCES

Linton (1995), p. 260
Taylor et al. (1993), p. 632

12 CORRECT ANSWER: 4

1. Leaving the call bell on the bedside table may make it inaccessible to the client in traction, particularly if the table is cluttered or out of reach.
2. If the call bell is to remain accessible and within the client's visual field, it needs to be in front of him. The headboard is not in front of the client and may not be within reach.
3. The side rail of a client's bed may not always be in the raised position and would not guarantee accessibility of the call bell by the client.
4. To be accessible, the call bell must be within reach and within the client's field of vision. To attach it to the trapeze bar would meet both criteria.

CLASSIFICATION

Competency Category:	Client Care – Implementation
Taxonomic Level:	Application
Client Age:	Adult

REFERENCES

Sorrentino (1992), p. 176
Timby & Lewis (1992), pp. 697–698

CASE 3

13 CORRECT ANSWER: 1

1. Cold, clammy skin is a manifestation of cardiogenic shock, a life-threatening complication of myocardial infarction.
2. A rapid, thready pulse, not a full, bounding pulse, is a manifestation of cardiogenic shock.
3. Cardiogenic shock is manifested by hypotension, not hypertension.
4. The decreased blood flow associated with cardiogenic shock results in lethargy, not increased muscular activity.

CLASSIFICATION

Competency Category:	Client Care – Assessment
Taxonomic Level:	Critical Thinking
Client Age:	Adult

REFERENCES

Phipps et al. (1991), p. 715
Suddarth (1991), p. 334

14 CORRECT ANSWER: 1

1. If the radial pulse is irregular, the apical pulse should be assessed immediately as it provides a more accurate assessment of cardiac rate and rhythm.
2. Counting the radial pulse on the other wrist may provide additional information, but is not as beneficial as assessing the apical pulse.
3. Blood pressure, an indicator of circulatory status, should also be assessed. However, the pulse regularity should be fully addressed first.
4. The apical and radial pulses are assessed for a pulse deficit, the difference between the two rates, not the two rhythms.

CLASSIFICATION

Competency Category: Client Care – Assessment
Taxonomic Level: Application
Client Age: Adult

REFERENCES

Potter & Perry (1993), p. 477
Taylor et al. (1993), p. 403

15 CORRECT ANSWER: 1

1. Individuals who have impaired awareness lose orientation first to time, then place, then person. Determining if the client is oriented to person by asking her name would provide the best assessment.
2. Asking the client what she ate for breakfast assesses her memory, not her level of orientation.
3. Asking the client about her opinion of a television program assesses her interaction with her environment, not her level of orientation.
4. Asking the client to add two numbers determines if she has the ability to compute in logical thought processes, not her level of orientation.

CLASSIFICATION

Competency Category: Client Care – Assessment
Taxonomic Level: Application
Client Age: Adult

REFERENCES

Potter & Perry (1993), pp. 597–599
Taylor et al. (1993), pp. 463–464

16 CORRECT ANSWER: 3

1. The client's name does not have to be included in the documentation as all data on the chart relate to one specific client.
2. Pain is subjective, and information about subjective data is obtained by interview.
3. The behavior noted is specific and the documentation includes objective as well as subjective data.
4. The client's name does not need to be noted in the documentation as all information on this chart pertains to the one client. Also, "restless" does not indicate an objective statement that has been validated.

CLASSIFICATION

Competency Category: Communication Skills
Taxonomic Level: Knowledge/Comprehension
Client Age: Adult

REFERENCES

McCarthy et al. (1994), p. 22
Smith (1992), pp. 89–90

17 CORRECT ANSWER: 2

1. Emergency resuscitation teams are on call at all times and are notified when an emergency situation arises.
2. It is the responsibility of practical nurses/nursing assistants to know at all times where emergency equipment is kept and how to use it.
3. The cart needs to be kept in a designated location so it is available for any client emergencies. In addition, placing the cart near the client would increase her anxiety.
4. The practical nurse/nursing assistant is responsible for knowing how emergency equipment works. Practicing with the equipment is not appropriate when an emergency is imminent.

CLASSIFICATION

Competency Category:	Client Care – Assessment
Taxonomic Level:	Knowledge/Comprehension
Client Age:	Adult

REFERENCES

McCarthy et al. (1994), p. 59
Rosdahl (1991), p. 299

18 CORRECT ANSWER: 4

1. Expressions of grief by the family should not be discouraged. The practical nurse/nursing assistant should support the act of grieving by the family rather than telling them not to get upset.
2. Family members become fatigued and should be encouraged to take breaks away from the dying person rather than being told to stay at the bedside.
3. Family members should be encouraged to interact with the dying family member in as normal a manner as possible, and not told how to speak.
4. The practical nurse/nursing assistant should carry out nursing procedures in the family's presence as much as possible.

CLASSIFICATION

Competency Category:	Client Care – Implementation
Taxonomic Level:	Affective
Client Age:	Adult

REFERENCES

Potter & Perry (1993), p. 879
Timby & Lewis (1992), p. 763

CASE 4

19 CORRECT ANSWER: 2

1. Normal respirations for an adolescent at rest are 16–18 breaths/min.
2. Bradypnea describes the rate of breathing that is abnormally slow.
3. Dyspnea describes breathing that is difficult.
4. Cheyne-Stokes respirations are irregular with alternating periods of apnea and hyperventilation.

CLASSIFICATION

Competency Category:	Client Care – Assessment
Taxonomic Level:	Knowledge/Comprehension
Client Age:	Child & Adolescent

REFERENCES
Craven & Hirnle (1992), pp. 363–364
Potter & Perry (1993), pp. 487–488

20 CORRECT ANSWER: 3

1. Contacting the school counselor is a breach of client confidentiality and is not the most appropriate contact for information on the client.
2. Contacting the client's peers is a breach of client confidentiality and is not the most appropriate contact for information on the client.
3. Parents are the most appropriate source of information, particularly when the client is an adolescent and in a depressed state.
4. Contacting the client's teacher is a breach of client confidentiality and is not the most appropriate contact for information on the client.

CLASSIFICATION

Competency Category:	Communication Skills
Taxonomic Level:	Knowledge/Comprehension
Client Age:	Child & Adolescent

REFERENCES
Rawlins et al. (1993), pp. 755–756
Townsend (1993), p. 357

21 CORRECT ANSWER: 1

1. Suicidal thought indicates a high safety risk. When assessing the safety of a depressed client, the practical nurse/nursing assistant should ask direct questions to obtain specific data.
2. Asking the client what he knows about depression does not address the safety issue.
3. This question is not assessing safety risk because it is not dealing with the situation.
4. Personal care could be a low level safety issue, but it is of less concern than the client's mental status.

CLASSIFICATION

Competency Category: Communication Skills
Taxonomic Level: Application
Client Age: Child & Adolescent

REFERENCES
Rawlins et al. (1993), pp. 100–101
Townsend (1993), p. 384

22 CORRECT ANSWER: 4

1. A depressed client does not respond well to logic. In addition, 24 hours is not a long time to go without food.
2. Depressed clients require socialization to assist them with their recovery. Therefore, the practical nurse/nursing assistant should encourage the client to eat with others.
3. The removal of privileges is a form of punishment. It is not the preferred approach when dealing with depressed clients.
4. The practical nurse/nursing assistant should respect the client's food preferences, which may lead to increasing his nutritional intake.

CLASSIFICATION

Competency Category: Client Care – Implementation
Taxonomic Level: Application
Client Age: Child & Adolescent

REFERENCES
Poleman & Peckenpaugh (1991), p. 187
Wilson & Kneisl (1992), p. 310

23 CORRECT ANSWER: 2

1. A pass to go home would not ensure the client's socialization and could pose a safety risk.
2. Accompanying the client to the patient lounge is an appropriate action because the practical nurse/nursing assistant could be a bridge through which the adolescent can safely communicate with others. It also provides the practical nurse/nursing assistant with an opportunity to assess the client's progress and monitor his safety.
3. Movie passes would not necessarily promote the client's socialization with others. In addition, it may be a safety risk for the client to leave the facility.
4. A depressed client requires more than a schedule of events to promote the socialization process.

CLASSIFICATION

Competency Category:	Communication Skills
Taxonomic Level:	Application
Client Age:	Child & Adolescent

REFERENCES
Rawlins et al. (1993), p. 765
Wilson & Kneisl (1992), p. 861

CASE 5

24 CORRECT ANSWER: 4

1. Hypotension, not hypertension, is a manifestation of shock.
2. Pallor, not flushed skin, is a manifestation of shock.
3. Hypotension, rather than hypertension, is a manifestation of shock.
4. Diaphoresis and hypotension are manifestations of shock.

CLASSIFICATION

Competency Category:	Client Care – Assessment
Taxonomic Level:	Knowledge/Comprehension
Client Age:	Adult

REFERENCES
May & Mahlmeister (1994), p. 714
Phillips (1991), p. 315

25 CORRECT ANSWER: 2

1. Elevating the legs of a client who has fainted does not increase blood pressure and would not be appropriate. In addition, the supine position is unsafe because it would not maintain the client's airway.
2. A client who has just fainted is likely still unconscious, and should be placed in the lateral position to maintain her airway. As well, the client should be assessed immediately for injuries.
3. Positioning to maintain the client's airway takes priority over checking lochia and vital signs.
4. Positioning to maintain the client's airway takes priority over checking for injuries and taking a pulse.

CLASSIFICATION

Competency Category:	Client Care – Planning
Taxonomic Level:	Critical Thinking
Client Age:	Adult

REFERENCES

May & Mahlmeister (1994), p. 717

Phillips (1991), p. 315

26 CORRECT ANSWER: 1

1. As blood volume decreases, the heart rate increases to compensate. When enough blood is lost, the quality of the pulse becomes weaker.
2. The quality of the pulse becomes weaker, not fuller, due to blood loss.
3. The rate of the pulse increases, rather than decreases, during blood loss.
4. The rate of the pulse increases and the quality weakens during blood loss.

CLASSIFICATION

Competency Category:	Client Care – Assessment
Taxonomic Level:	Application
Client Age:	Adult

REFERENCES

May & Mahlmeister (1994), p. 715

Reeder et al. (1992), p. 947

27 CORRECT ANSWER: 1

1. Lochial flow indicates how the uterus is involuting. The breast assessment determines the ability to nourish the infant.
2. Bladder control is of less importance than the condition of the breasts. As well, loss of bladder control is unlikely in a normal delivery.
3. Emotional stability and condition of the nipples are of less importance than lochial flow and condition of the breasts.
4. Bladder control is of less importance than lochial flow. As well, loss of bladder control is unlikely in a normal delivery.

CLASSIFICATION

Competency Category:	Client Care – Assessment
Taxonomic Level:	Application
Client Age:	Adult

REFERENCES

May & Mahlmeister (1994), p. 807

Phillips (1991), p. 285

28 CORRECT ANSWER: 2

1. Using a clean cloth to wash the perineum is only appropriate once healing has occurred.
2. **Cleansing from front to back with warm water prevents contamination of the vagina with feces. Warm water is recommended if no infection exists.**
3. Cleansing should be done from front to back.
4. Wiping with dry gauze or tissues is not sufficient to prevent bacterial growth; it is necessary to cleanse with water or antiseptic.

CLASSIFICATION

Competency Category: Client Care – Implementation
Taxonomic Level: Knowledge/Comprehension
Client Age: Adult

REFERENCES

May & Mahlmeister (1994), pp. 822–823
Phillips (1991), pp. 284–285

CASE 6

29 CORRECT ANSWER: 2

1. Reassuring the client that sexual function will be unaffected by the surgery provides false reassurance.
2. **The client needs to be aware of what to expect postoperatively. To clarify questions and to avoid misunderstandings, asking the client is the best approach in assessing what needs to be taught.**
3. Preoperative fasting is usually initiated after midnight.
4. The client can be told about the recovery room. However, it is inappropriate to physically orient her.

CLASSIFICATION

Competency Category: Client Care – Implementation
Taxonomic Level: Application
Client Age: Adult

REFERENCES

deWit & Keane (1992), pp. 224–229
Sorrentino (1992), pp. 367–373

30 CORRECT ANSWER: 4

1. The client should be instructed to breathe in through her nose and out through her mouth.
2. Deep breathing and coughing exercises are usually performed every 1–2 hours to prevent respiratory complications.
3. The client should inhale through her nose and exhale through pursed lips.
4. **Splinting an abdominal incision while coughing will decrease discomfort due to forced expiratory movement.**

CLASSIFICATION

Competency Category: Client Care – Implementation
Taxonomic Level: Application
Client Age: Adult

REFERENCES

deWit & Keane (1992), pp. 241–243
Sorrentino (1992), p. 375

31 CORRECT ANSWER: 3

1. If the practical nurse/nursing assistant chooses to use gloves, they should be sterile to maintain surgical asepsis.
2. The incision is cleansed from the least contaminated area to prevent the introduction of microorganisms.
3. A separate swab prevents contaminating previously cleansed areas and maintains the principles of surgical asepsis.
4. Handwashing is required before beginning the procedure and not at this stage.

CLASSIFICATION

Competency Category:	Client Care – Implementation
Taxonomic Level:	Application
Client Age:	Adult

REFERENCES

Potter & Perry (1993), pp. 1668–1674
Suddarth (1991), pp. 72–75

32 CORRECT ANSWER: 4

1. The urinary meatus should be cleansed prior to the catheter to cleanse from the area of least to most contamination.
2. Looped tubing encourages poor drainage and backflow, which promotes the risk of infection.
3. Sterile gloves are unnecessary when caring for an indwelling catheter.
4. Urine flow must be downhill to avoid reflux.

CLASSIFICATION

Competency Category:	Client Care – Implementation
Taxonomic Level:	Application
Client Age:	Adult

REFERENCES

Potter & Perry (1993), pp. 1371–1374
Suddarth (1991), p. 669

33 CORRECT ANSWER: 1

1. Jerky motions increase the risk of injury, so it is best to use smooth and even movements.
2. Weight to be lifted should be as close to the practical nurse/nursing assistant as possible to use the lifting force of the practical nurse/nursing assistant.
3. The height of the bed should be at the level of the practical nurse's/nursing assistant's waist to avoid unnecessary bending.
4. The practical nurse's/nursing assistant's upper trunk should be erect to allow multiple muscle groups to work in a synchronized manner.

CLASSIFICATION

Competency Category:	Client Care – Implementation
Taxonomic Level:	Application
Client Age:	Adult

REFERENCES

Potter & Perry (1993), p. 1488
Sorrentino (1992), p. 147

34 CORRECT ANSWER: 2

1. The practical nurse/nursing assistant needs to know the last time an analgesic was given prior to activities, not the anesthetic.
2. Assistance from another health care team member is necessary because Mrs. Long is too heavy for one person to move safely.
3. Using a mechanical lift does not promote postoperative ambulation.
4. Attaching the urinary drainage bag to Mrs. Long's gown is unnecessary because she is not leaving the bedside.

CLASSIFICATION

Competency Category:	Client Care – Implementation
Taxonomic Level:	Application
Client Age:	Adult

REFERENCES

Potter & Perry (1993), p. 1495
Suddarth (1991), p. 600

CASE 7

35 CORRECT ANSWER: 1

1. Vitamin C promotes healing and is of particular importance in the malnourished.
2. High-fiber diets do promote elimination, but the client's primary problem is poor healing, not constipation.
3. Foods containing a large amount of cellulose are digested more slowly than foods that have had the cellulose broken down by preparation and cooking.
4. Less preparation time is not the most important reason for encouraging the client to eat fresh fruits and vegetables.

CLASSIFICATION

Competency Category:	Client Care – Implementation
Taxonomic Level:	Critical Thinking
Client Age:	Older Adult

REFERENCES

Burke & Walsh (1992), p. 145
Poleman & Peckenpaugh (1991), p. 64

36 CORRECT ANSWER: 1

1. It is the duty of the person performing the procedure to verify that consent for the care is given.
2. Signing a consent form is part of obtaining consent, rather than affirming consent, and is usually reserved for invasive procedures.
3. A witness is not necessary to affirm consent.
4. As long as the client is competent, there is no need to consult the family for affirmation of consent.

CLASSIFICATION

Competency Category:	Professional and Personal Responsibilities
Taxonomic Level:	Application
Client Age:	Older Adult

REFERENCES

Morris (1991), pp. 117–123
Smith (1992), p. 68

37 CORRECT ANSWER: 3

1. Oral antibiotics may upset the client's stomach, but this is not the reason why he is on I.V.
2. It is not true that giving antibiotics in I.V. form is more economical.
3. The information on antibiotics is true, and appropriate health information should be offered to the client, especially when asked.
4. The practical nurse/nursing assistant does not address the client's question with this response.

CLASSIFICATION

Competency Category:	Client Care – Implementation
Taxonomic Level:	Application
Client Age:	Older Adult

REFERENCES

Redman (1993), pp. 1–9
Smith (1992), pp. 34–37

38 CORRECT ANSWER: 4

1. Dry skin is normal and can be helped with the use of skin emollients. Dry skin does not require special care.
2. Lowering of the arch does not necessarily cause problems or require special care.
3. Shoes may be too loose with loss of subcutaneous tissue but, until redness is noted, this is not a problem.
4. Hard, thickened nails result from inadequate nutrition and/or poor circulation and require the attention of a podiatrist.

CLASSIFICATION

Competency Category:	Client Care – Implementation
Taxonomic Level:	Application
Client Age:	Older Adult

REFERENCES

Ebersole & Hess (1990), p. 251
Perry & Potter (1994), p. 162

39 CORRECT ANSWER: 1

1. Open wounds require sterile technique.
2. Open areas should be cared for using sterile technique.
3. Open wounds require sterile technique.
4. Open ulcers should be cared for using sterile technique.

CLASSIFICATION

Competency Category:	Client Care – Implementation
Taxonomic Level:	Application
Client Age:	Older Adult

REFERENCES

Kozier et al. (1991), p. 1293
Perry & Potter (1994), p. 28

40 CORRECT ANSWER: 1

1. Asking the client what he thinks might be behind the lack of healing determines his readiness to learn as well as his present level of understanding. It is also an open-ended question.
2. Indicating to the client that he is capable of learning to change his own dressing is a positive interaction, but it is not the first one. Readiness to learn should be determined first.
3. Questioning the client about being malnourished is a very direct approach and does not determine his readiness to learn.
4. The practical nurse/nursing assistant should discuss with the client the side effects of medications taken, but not as a first step.

CLASSIFICATION

Competency Category:	Communication Skills
Taxonomic Level:	Critical Thinking
Client Age:	Older Adult

REFERENCES
Kozier et al. (1991), p. 284
Long (1992), pp. 192–194

INDEPENDENT QUESTIONS

41 CORRECT ANSWER: 1

1. Two people should always be present when using mechanical lifting devices.
2. The brakes should be applied when the client is being lifted off the bed and when lowered into the chair, tub, etc. If the brakes were applied during the transfer, the lifting device could not be moved within the room.
3. The base of support is kept wide whenever possible to ensure greater stability and safety.
4. Equipment should be checked prior to use to ensure safety. The practical nurse/nursing assistant could also check it after use, but this is of less importance.

CLASSIFICATION

Competency Category:	Client Care – Implementation
Taxonomic Level:	Application
Client Age:	General

REFERENCES
Caldwell & Hegner (1989), p. 195
Kozier et al. (1991), pp. 923–924

42 CORRECT ANSWER: 1

1. High-Fowler's position is the most appropriate position for clients with dyspnea as it provides for maximum lung expansion.
2. Low-Fowler's is not as effective as high-Fowler's position in providing for lung expansion.
3. A supine position will allow the abdomen to put more upward pressure on the diaphragm, in effect causing more dyspnea by decreasing the maximum intrathoracic space for lung expansion.
4. A right lateral position will limit diaphragmatic movement and is not the position of choice for a dyspneic client.

CLASSIFICATION

Competency Category:	Client Care – Implementation
Taxonomic Level:	Knowledge/Comprehension
Client Age:	Older Adult

REFERENCES

Kozier et al. (1991), p. 1105
Potter & Perry (1993), p. 1245

43 CORRECT ANSWER: 1

1. Finger foods will likely increase self-feeding behaviors because a confused client may not remember how to use utensils.
2. Demonstrations are often not comprehended by clients with Alzheimer disease.
3. Confused clients with Alzheimer disease do not tolerate new foods well. They are more likely to eat familiar foods.
4. Many food choices increase confusion and can be frustrating for clients with Alzheimer disease. A better option would be to reduce the number of choices.

CLASSIFICATION

Competency Category:	Client Care – Implementation
Taxonomic Level:	Application
Client Age:	Older Adult

REFERENCES

Birchenall & Streight (1993), pp. 269–270
Hamdy et al. (1994), pp. 171–172

44 CORRECT ANSWER: 2

1. A pain in the calf may demonstrate a cramp from exercising too vigorously. However, encouraging the client to continue exercising puts her at risk if she has a thrombosis.
2. Postoperative calf pain is often the initial manifestation of a thrombosis. This potentially hazardous finding should be reported to the nurse-in-charge immediately.
3. Removing antiembolic stockings may threaten the client's safety if she has a thrombosis.
4. The client's pain should be reported as it may signify a thrombosis.

CLASSIFICATION

Competency Category:	Client Care – Implementation
Taxonomic Level:	Application
Client Age:	Older Adult

REFERENCES

deWit & Keane (1992), pp. 511–512
Timby & Lewis (1992), pp. 447–448

45 CORRECT ANSWER: 3

1. Narrow, pencil-shaped feces may indicate obstruction or rapid peristalsis.
2. Mucous-coated feces may indicate an irritation and are not considered normal.
3. Characteristic odor is a result of the food ingested and is considered normal.
4. Black, tarry feces indicate iron ingestion or upper gastrointestinal bleeding.

CLASSIFICATION

Competency Category:	Client Care – Assessment
Taxonomic Level:	Knowledge/Comprehension
Client Age:	General

REFERENCES

Hood & Dincher (1992), p. 438
Potter & Perry (1993), p. 1401

46 CORRECT ANSWER: 2

1. The practical nurse/nursing assistant has no idea who put up the side rails, or how the client ended up on the floor. This is inappropriate recording on an incident report, where objective facts are recorded.
2. This is the best choice as it indicates the objective data the practical nurse/nursing assistant observed.
3. It is judgmental to state the side rails were put up in error, and it is inappropriate to be judgmental in the recording of an incident.
4. The practical nurse/nursing assistant is assuming the client climbed over the side rails, and it is inappropriate to record personal assumptions on an incident report.

CLASSIFICATION

Competency Category:	Communication Skills
Taxonomic Level:	Knowledge/Comprehension
Client Age:	General

REFERENCES

Craven & Hirnle (1992), p. 165
Hill (1993), pp. 248–249

47 CORRECT ANSWER: 4

1. Louder sounds suffer more distortion than those of usual volume. It is also recommended that the practical nurse/nursing assistant face clients who are hearing impaired, in order that they can take advantage of nonverbal cues.
2. Higher pitches are harder to understand. Therefore, lower pitch is recommended when speaking to a client who is hearing impaired.
3. The client may not be able to read lips well, so there is no guarantee that he will fully understand the instructions or "see" the same words that are spoken.
4. As preoperative instructions are important to the recovery of the client, it is essential that they are understood. Writing the instructions on a paper ensures that he will receive all the necessary information.

CLASSIFICATION

Competency Category:	Communication Skills
Taxonomic Level:	Application
Client Age:	Older Adult

REFERENCES

Birchenall & Streight (1993), p. 73
Eliopoulos (1993), pp. 263–264

48 CORRECT ANSWER: 3

1. Pigmentation changes are normal age-related changes.
2. Thinning, graying hair is a normal age-related change.
3. Improperly fitting dentures could interfere with the client's ability to eat, could cause mouth sores, and are not an expected age-related change.
4. Folding, sagging skin is a normal age-related change.

CLASSIFICATION

Competency Category:	Client Care – Assessment
Taxonomic Level:	Knowledge/Comprehension
Client Age:	Older Adult

REFERENCES

Ebersole & Hess (1990), p. 170
Perry & Potter (1994), p. 146

CORRECT ANSWER: 3

1. The surgery is frightening to the client regardless of how minor it is. Stating this belittles her anxiety and does not demonstrate concern.
2. This response reinforces the client's fear of surgery and inappropriately shifts the focus to the practical nurse's/nursing assistant's experience with surgery.
3. Admitting that the surgery is frightening acknowledges the client's feelings. The practical nurse/nursing assistant further opens up the route of communication by offering to help.
4. Reminding the client that she has had surgery before does not address her feelings. Building on her previous knowledge of surgery is very appropriate. However, feelings need to be recognized.

CLASSIFICATION

Competency Category:	Communication Skills
Taxonomic Level:	Affective
Client Age:	Older Adult

REFERENCES
Long (1992), p. 24
Smith (1992), pp. 95–96, 98

50 **CORRECT ANSWER: 2**

1. There is no indication that a specimen of the emesis is required at this time.
2. Universal precautions demand that gown and gloves be worn when there is a likelihood of contamination with body fluids.
3. Leaving the emesis on the floor creates a safety hazard for the client and health care team.
4. Because there is a low risk of being splashed in the face with blood or body fluids, a mask is not necessary.

CLASSIFICATION

Competency Category:	Client Care – Implementation
Taxonomic Level:	Application
Client Age:	Child & Adolescent

REFERENCES
Smeltzer & Bare (1992), p. 1376
Taylor et al. (1993), p. 526

51 CORRECT ANSWER: 3

1. Washing hands after all client care is not incorrect, but wearing gloves during the care of a client with blood in the urine is more important.
2. Double bagging is not required for catheter disposal unless contamination of the outside of the bag cannot be avoided. A sturdy, impervious bag is usually adequate.
3. Disposable gloves protect the caregiver from blood-contaminated urine, thus maintaining universal precautions when caring for the catheter.
4. Gowns do not need to be worn unless it is likely there will be splashes of blood or other body fluids contaminated with blood.

CLASSIFICATION

Competency Category:	Client Care – Implementation
Taxonomic Level:	Application
Client Age:	Older Adult

REFERENCES
Kozier et al. (1991), p. 1221
Potter & Perry (1993), pp. 422–429

52 CORRECT ANSWER: 4

1. Incorrect directions may have been a contributing factor. The main error that should be documented is a failure by the practical nurse/nursing assistant to verify the physician's orders prior to administering the enema.
2. It is correct to administer the enema to Mrs. Talbot, but it is wrong to assume that both clients will have appropriate bowel evacuation. Mrs. Sands has received an enema in error.
3. Mrs. Sands has the right to know that an error was committed in her prescribed treatment, but the practical nurse/nursing assistant should first consult with the nurse-in-charge.
4. The documentation of circumstances and events on the appropriate agency forms will provide information for the review of the error and subsequent actions for quality assurance and risk management by the facility.

CLASSIFICATION

Competency Category:	Professional and Personal Responsibilities
Taxonomic Level:	Critical Thinking
Client Age:	General

REFERENCES
Kozier et al. (1991), pp. 154, 158
Potter & Perry (1993), pp. 298–299

53 CORRECT ANSWER: 3

1. Sebaceous gland function diminishes with age. Therefore, brushing the client's hair will not likely make it shine.
2. A wide-toothed comb is more suitable than a fine-toothed comb for curly hair.
3. A wide-toothed comb is most suitable for curly hair.
4. Putting her hair in a hairnet would likely increase tangles in long hair.

CLASSIFICATION

Competency Category: Client Care – Implementation
Taxonomic Level: Application
Client Age: Older Adult

REFERENCES

Bolander (1994), pp. 930–931
Potter & Perry (1993), pp. 850–851

54 CORRECT ANSWER: 3

1. Having her grandson help her with the yardwork is not the most important piece of data to document.
2. Taking the bus is not the most important piece of data to document.
3. The fact that the client uses a raised toilet seat indicates that she has decreased function and requires assistance to maintain her safety.
4. Wearing slacks and sweaters is not the most important piece of data to document.

CLASSIFICATION

Competency Category: Client Care – Assessment
Taxonomic Level: Application
Client Age: Older Adult

REFERENCES

Bolander (1994), p. 409
Phipps et al. (1991), p. 2003

55 CORRECT ANSWER: 3

1. A disposable glove is needed to remove dentures in order to reduce the transmission of microorganisms.
2. Hot water may cause the dentures to warp.
3. Dentures should be held over water when brushing to decrease the risk of breakage if they are dropped.
4. Soaking the dentures in mouthwash does not clean the dentures properly.

be damaged by bending or twisting

CLASSIFICATION

Competency Category: Client Care – Implementation
Taxonomic Level: Application
Client Age: Older Adult

REFERENCES

deWit & Keane (1992), p. 415
Potter & Perry (1993), p. 1055

56 CORRECT ANSWER: 1

1. When prioritizing care, the practical nurse/nursing assistant should consider the level of risk, the unknown factors, routine client care, and scheduled appointments in that order. In this situation, the client returning from the recovery room has the highest level of risk and, therefore, should be the first priority.
2. The client in pain is considered an unknown factor and, therefore, would be the practical nurse's/nursing assistant's second priority.
3. The client with a physiotherapy appointment is considered a scheduled appointment and, therefore, would be the practical nurse's/nursing assistant's last priority.
4. The clients' meal trays are considered routine client care and, therefore, would be the practical nurse's/nursing assistant's third priority.

CLASSIFICATION

Competency Category:	Client Care – Planning
Taxonomic Level:	Critical Thinking
Client Age:	General

REFERENCES

Potter & Perry (1993), p. 188
Sorrentino (1992), pp. 21–22

57 CORRECT ANSWER: 4

1. To dismiss the client's distress as inconsequential is unlikely to make the client feel more comfortable with the practical nurse/nursing assistant and will invalidate his feelings.
2. Problem solving for the client may resolve the physical concern, but will also make him feel more dependent. It is not likely to foster the level of communication that enhances rapport.
3. Minimizing the situation may defuse the tension, but is unlikely to enhance rapport.
4. Demonstrating empathy allows the practical nurse/nursing assistant to indicate care for the client's feelings. Empathy provides a link between two human beings that decreases isolation and enhances rapport.

CLASSIFICATION

Competency Category:	Communication Skills
Taxonomic Level:	Affective
Client Age:	Adult

REFERENCES

Long (1992), pp. 24–25
Smith (1992), pp. 95–105

130

58 CORRECT ANSWER: 2

1. Increasing loss of sensation would predispose the development of a pressure sore but is not considered stage one.
2. A reddened area that stays red even after the pressure is relieved is stage one of pressure sore development.
3. A cyanotic area is considered stage two in pressure sore development.
4. Increasing edema is a predisposing factor in pressure sore development, but does not indicate the first stage in pressure sore development.

CLASSIFICATION

Competency Category:	Client Care – Assessment
Taxonomic Level:	Knowledge/Comprehension
Client Age:	Adult

REFERENCES

Taylor et al. (1993), p. 626
Timby & Lewis (1992), p. 462

59 CORRECT ANSWER: 3

1. It is inappropriate for the practical nurse/nursing assistant to leave the postoperative client who requires nursing care.
2. Postoperative vomiting with evidence of dark red blood does not need to be reported immediately to the nurse-in-charge. However, it does need to be documented.
3. It is most appropriate to assess the client at this time and report and record the findings.
4. Suctioning is not recommended for a client who has had a tonsillectomy as the operative site may be disrupted.

CLASSIFICATION

Competency Category:	Client Care – Assessment
Taxonomic Level:	Application
Client Age:	Child & Adolescent

REFERENCES

Thompson (1990), p. 643
Whaley & Wong (1993), p. 718

60 CORRECT ANSWER: 4

1. A one-person transfer is an unsafe procedure for a client who feels weak.
2. A two-person lift is unnecessary because the client is able to bear weight.
3. A mechanical lift is unnecessary because the client is able to bear weight.
4. A two-person standing transfer is the safest approach if the client feels weak.

CLASSIFICATION

Competency Category:	Client Care – Implementation
Taxonomic Level:	Application
Client Age:	Older Adult

REFERENCES

Kozier et al. (1993), pp. 466–474
Sorrentino (1992), pp. 158–167

61 CORRECT ANSWER: 3

1. Stating that he will never play hockey again is a reasonable initial response to a painful injury.
2. Awakening from sleep and talking does not necessarily indicate a deterioration in level of consciousness.
3. Irritability is a symptom of decreasing level of consciousness.
4. Asking to be discharged may indicate that he does not understand the reason for his continued monitoring, not that his level of consciousness is deteriorating.

CLASSIFICATION

Competency Category:	Client Care – Assessment
Taxonomic Level:	Application
Client Age:	Adult

REFERENCES

Phipps et al. (1991), p. 1759
Potter & Perry (1993), p. 597

62 CORRECT ANSWER: 1

1. Apple juice and gelatin are considered part of a clear fluid diet and are suitable for a 3-year-old child.
2. Popsicles are included in a clear, fluid diet but milk drinks are full fluids.
3. Gelatin is included in a clear, fluid diet but ice cream is a full fluid.
4. Tea and broth are included in a clear, fluid diet but tea may not be appropriate for a 3-year-old child.

CLASSIFICATION

Competency Category:	Client Care – Implementation
Taxonomic Level:	Application
Client Age:	Child & Adolescent

REFERENCES

Dudek (1993), p. 354
Mahan et al. (1992), pp. 426–427

63 CORRECT ANSWER: 2

1. All resuscitation equipment is not in the oxygen storage room.
2. Each nursing station has an emergency setup with equipment for emergencies.
3. The medication room does not always contain emergency equipment.
4. Emergency equipment is kept on every unit, not just on the intensive care unit and in the emergency department.

CLASSIFICATION

Competency Category:	Client Care – Assessment
Taxonomic Level:	Knowledge/Comprehension
Client Age:	Adult

REFERENCES

McCarthy et al. (1994), p. 59
Rosdahl (1991), p. 299

CORRECT ANSWER: 3

1. A foam ring is thought to increase the risk of pressure ulcer formation because it increases ischemia.
2. Having the client sleep on her side would increase the possibility of developing pressure ulcers on the hips.
3. Changing position frequently relieves pressure around superficial capillaries and allows tissues to compensate for temporary ischemia. It decreases the possibility of pressure ulcer formation.
4. Warm water helps promote capillary blood flow, but sitting in a hard tub could increase the pressure in the coccygeal area.

CLASSIFICATION

Competency Category: Client Care – Implementation
Taxonomic Level: Application
Client Age: Adult

REFERENCES
Ignatavicius & Bayne (1991), p. 510
Perry & Potter (1994), pp. 121–122

 CORRECT ANSWER: 4

1. Attending an inservice on client aggression is more for the protection of the caregiver than for protection of the client.
2. Maintaining an optimal level of physical fitness is more for the protection of the caregiver than for protection of the client.
3. Incident reports are completed primarily for the protection of the agency and staff rather than for protection of the client.
4. Medications should be checked three times to reduce administration errors. Medication errors are a safety issue for the client.

CLASSIFICATION

Competency Category: Client Care – Implementation
Taxonomic Level: Knowledge/Comprehension
Client Age: General

REFERENCES
Kozier et al. (1991), pp. 1265, 1269
Potter & Perry (1993), pp. 637–640, 675

66 CORRECT ANSWER: 4

1. False readings of blood pressure due to venous congestion of the arm may occur if readings are repeated immediately.
2. The practical nurse/nursing assistant should make another attempt to obtain the reading independently before seeking assistance from a health care team member.
3. The cuff does not need to be reapplied prior to rechecking a reading unless it is improperly positioned.
4. Repeating the reading after a short waiting period will allow for venous return and prevent venous congestion.

CLASSIFICATION

Competency Category: Client Care – Assessment
Taxonomic Level: Knowledge/Comprehension
Client Age: Older Adult

REFERENCES
Springhouse Corporation (1994), p. 269
Timby & Lewis (1992), pp. 267–269

67 CORRECT ANSWER: 4

1. The practical nurse/nursing assistant is not acting on the available opportunity to encourage the client to express herself.
2. It is too early in the interaction to suggest a visit from the breast cancer support group. The practical nurse/nursing assistant is capable of offering support and may be losing an opportunity for the client to talk.
3. Hollow repetition of the client's words is nontherapeutic.
4. Offering of self is a useful technique to use at the beginning of the interaction and demonstrates a commitment to helping the client.

CLASSIFICATION

Competency Category:	Communication Skills
Taxonomic Level:	Affective
Client Age:	Adult

REFERENCES

Bolander (1994), pp. 437–442
Smith (1992), p. 29

68 CORRECT ANSWER: 1

1. Normal respirations for an 18-month-old are 20–30 breaths/min and regular. A loose cough is not unusual with a diagnosis of an upper respiratory infection. These data must be recorded, but no further action is required.
2. There is no reason to notify a physician about the client's respiratory status because it is essentially normal.
3. The client's respiratory status is essentially normal, so a second opinion is not required.
4. Frequent reassessment by the practical nurse/nursing assistant of the client's respiratory status would only be appropriate if she were showing signs of increasing distress.

CLASSIFICATION

Competency Category:	Client Care – Assessment
Taxonomic Level:	Application
Client Age:	Child & Adolescent

REFERENCES

Thompson (1990), p. 501
Whaley & Wong (1993), p. 727

69 CORRECT ANSWER: 1

1. Pain is subjective and only the client can assess the degree of discomfort experienced.
2. Determining past pain history is important but it is not the most important approach to take when assessing postoperative pain.
3. Determining the client's usual approaches to pain management is important but it is not the most important information to consider when assessing postoperative pain.
4. Regardless of cultural influences, the client's perception of pain is the most important factor in assessing the pain.

CLASSIFICATION

Competency Category: Client Care – Assessment
Taxonomic Level: Application
Client Age: Older Adult

REFERENCES

Bolander (1994), pp. 963, 968
Rosdahl (1991), pp. 462–463

70 CORRECT ANSWER: 4

1. Asking the client if she is aware of the treatment for AIDS is inappropriate, because the practical nurse/nursing assistant should deal with the test itself and not assume that she has AIDS.
2. Asking the client if she is sexually active is an inappropriate question at this time, because it is not facilitating the client's understanding of the HIV test.
3. Asking the client if she would like to have her family notified is inappropriate, as this question implies that she will need some form of support. An HIV test can be a routine procedure for clients with a history of I.V. drug abuse.
4. The first step in assessing clients is to ask if they understand the purpose of a test. This question is a therapeutic communication technique.

CLASSIFICATION

Competency Category: Communication Skills
Taxonomic Level: Application
Client Age: General

REFERENCES

Townsend (1993), p. 72
Wilson & Kneisl (1992), p. 142

71 CORRECT ANSWER: 1

1. The client and her family need to decide together how they can help each other cope with this difficult time in their lives. This question demonstrates that the practical nurse/nursing assistant is gathering information for further assessment.
2. The assessment process needs to be conducted before any action can be implemented by the practical nurse/nursing assistant.
3. The practical nurse/nursing assistant passes responsibility to the pastoral care team too early in the process. In addition, the practical nurse/nursing assistant sounds judgmental by referring to the situation as a dilemma.
4. The practical nurse's/nursing assistant's viewpoint may not be objective.

CLASSIFICATION

Competency Category:	Client Care – Implementation
Taxonomic Level:	Critical Thinking
Client Age:	Older Adult

REFERENCES

Scherer (1991), pp. 151–152
Sorrentino (1992), p. 467

72 CORRECT ANSWER: 1

1. Recording an approach that was used successfully is the planning or developmental stage of a nursing care plan.
2. Relating the client's comments would be the assessment phase of developing a care plan.
3. Trying several approaches is the implementation phase of a care plan.
4. Identifying possible sources or precipitating factors of the client's behavior is the assessment phase of developing a care plan.

CLASSIFICATION

Competency Category:	Client Care – Planning
Taxonomic Level:	Application
Client Age:	Child & Adolescent

REFERENCES

Hegner & Caldwell (1992), pp. 118–123
Kozier et al. (1991), p. 167

73 CORRECT ANSWER: 1

1. Measuring abdominal girth at the client's umbilicus provides a consistent, accurate measurement.
2. Chest circumference is not included in the measurement of abdominal girth.
3. Placing the client on her back could aggravate the congestive heart failure.
4. The client is encouraged to relax and breathe normally when measuring abdominal girth to avoid distorting the abdominal measurement.

CLASSIFICATION

Competency Category:	Client Care – Assessment
Taxonomic Level:	Application
Client Age:	Adult

REFERENCES

Beare & Myers (1990), p. 1637
Lewis & Collier (1992), p. 1142

74 CORRECT ANSWER: 1

1. Diaper h.s. specifies the correct terminology, "at hour of sleep."
2. Diaper p.r.n. refers the care provider to diaper whenever necessary.
3. Diaper q.s. stands for as much as may be needed.
4. Diaper q.d. gives the direction to diaper daily, not at night.

CLASSIFICATION

Competency Category:	Communication Skills
Taxonomic Level:	Knowledge/Comprehension
Client Age:	Child & Adolescent

REFERENCES

Craven & Hirnle (1992), p. 151
Kozier et al. (1991), pp. 314–315

75 CORRECT ANSWER: 3

1. Four-year-olds are usually very attached to their parents, so it is inappropriate to ask the client's mother to leave.
2. Asking the client to wait 15 minutes is not appropriate because the concept of time is not fully understood by a 4-year-old child.
3. Four-year-olds are imaginative and like to pretend, so allowing her to play with the stethoscope will likely facilitate the rest of the examination.
4. Sitting quietly without appropriate distraction is difficult for a 4-year-old child.

CLASSIFICATION

Competency Category:	Client Care – Implementation
Taxonomic Level:	Application
Client Age:	Child & Adolescent

REFERENCES

Malasanos et al. (1990), pp. 610–611
Whaley & Wong (1993), pp. 130–131, 639

76 CORRECT ANSWER: 2

1. The care of surgical wounds requires surgical asepsis.
2. The maintenance of nasogastric tubes is a clean procedure and requires medical asepsis.
3. Indwelling urinary catheter insertions require surgical asepsis.
4. The removal of sutures requires surgical asepsis.

CLASSIFICATION

Competency Category:	Client Care – Implementation
Taxonomic Level:	Knowledge/Comprehension
Client Age:	Child & Adolescent

REFERENCES

Christensen & Kockrow (1994), pp. 189, 197
Potter & Perry (1993), p. 407

77 CORRECT ANSWER: 1

1. Verifying the order for a procedure is the first step in carrying it out.
2. Explaining the reason for a procedure follows the verification of an order.
3. Obtaining the equipment is a step that is carried out after the order has been verified.
4. Alternative approaches should be explored before the procedure is ordered. No further steps should be taken until after verification of the physician's order.

CLASSIFICATION

Competency Category:	Professional and Personal Responsibilities
Taxonomic Level:	Knowledge/Comprehension
Client Age:	Child & Adolescent

REFERENCES
Hegner & Caldwell (1992), p. 639
Perry & Potter (1994), p. 52

78 CORRECT ANSWER: 2

1. Economic status is an important factor affecting food availability but it is not influencing the client's ability to eat the food provided.
2. Personal preference is one major factor that determines what a person eats. Documentation would need to include this information.
3. Social status is a factor pertaining to food intake but it is not likely the most important to consider.
4. The client's environment does not usually influence food intake. It influences storage and preparation.

CLASSIFICATION

Competency Category:	Client Care – Assessment
Taxonomic Level:	Application
Client Age:	Older Adult

REFERENCES
Beckingham & DuGas (1993), p. 137
Stanhope & Lancaster (1992), p. 593

79 CORRECT ANSWER: 1

1. A drop in blood pressure indicates that there is a drop in blood volume as a result of internal bleeding. The body's attempt to oxygenate with less circulating blood results in an increased pulse rate.
2. Although increasing respirations may be indicative of shock secondary to internal bleeding, a drop in pulse rate is not.
3. Although blood pressure may be stable or slightly elevated in the initial stages of shock, it is so subtle that it would be impossible to detect. Respiratory rate increases to enhance oxygenation when blood volume falls.
4. Although blood pressure may be stable or slightly elevated in the initial stages of shock, it is so subtle that it would be impossible to detect. Pulse becomes rapid and thready to compensate for diminished blood volume.

CLASSIFICATION

Competency Category:	Client Care – Assessment
Taxonomic Level:	Application
Client Age:	Adult

REFERENCES
Hood & Dincher (1992), p. 95
Phipps et al. (1991), p. 582

80 CORRECT ANSWER: 2

1. A urine collection device can be placed in the toilet; therefore, there is no need for a commode to be placed in the client's room.
2. If the client is able, her help should be enlisted when keeping track of intake and output.
3. Intake and output should be kept on a record placed at the bedside so anyone can access it and assist with the documentation.
4. There is no need to remove the water pitcher as long as the amount of water consumed is recorded.

CLASSIFICATION

Competency Category:	Client Care – Assessment
Taxonomic Level:	Knowledge/Comprehension
Client Age:	Adult

REFERENCES

Springhouse Corporation (1994), p. 96
Timby & Lewis (1992), pp. 644–645

81 CORRECT ANSWER: 3

1. Each time the dressing is changed, it should be charted.
2. There is no description of the amount or type of drainage.
3. This is an appropriate example of charting because it includes the location of the dressing and the amount and type of drainage.
4. This example does not include the location of the dressing or the amount or type of drainage.

CLASSIFICATION

Competency Category:	Communication Skills
Taxonomic Level:	Knowledge/Comprehension
Client Age:	General

REFERENCES

Potter & Perry (1993), pp. 1672–1673
Rosdahl (1991), pp. 273, 278

82 CORRECT ANSWER: 2

1. It may be difficult for the client to remove the bedpan himself due to his physical limitations.
2. It is safer and easier to roll the client onto his side because of his physical limitations.
3. The client is overweight and elderly. It is unlikely that he will be capable of lifting his buttocks off the bed by flexing his knees and exerting muscle control.
4. The client is arthritic, overweight, and elderly. It is unlikely that he will be able to support his weight with his arms.

CLASSIFICATION

Competency Category:	Client Care – Implementation
Taxonomic Level:	Application
Client Age:	Older Adult

REFERENCES

Kozier et al. (1991), pp. 1167–1168
Taylor et al. (1993), p. 917

83 CORRECT ANSWER: 1

1. Redness along the vein is a sign of phlebitis.
2. Infiltration is characterized by swelling and pallor.
3. Bacteremia is characterized by clinical manifestations of a systemic nature (e.g., nausea, chills, malaise).
4. Inflammation is a general term. Phlebitis is a more accurate descriptor.

CLASSIFICATION

Competency Category:	Client Care – Assessment
Taxonomic Level:	Knowledge/Comprehension
Client Age:	Child & Adolescent

REFERENCES

Potter & Perry (1993), pp. 1315–1316
Suddarth (1991), pp. 86–87

84 CORRECT ANSWER: 3

1. The practical nurse/nursing assistant should realize that the daughter knows her mother is going to die, so asking her what she knows about her mother is avoiding the issue.
2. The child has indicated a desire to talk about a painful situation. Therefore, putting her off would increase her stress and create a sense of mystery.
3. In communicating with a child about death, the practical nurse/nursing assistant must be truthful, offer no false hope, and be available to listen to the child's concerns.
4. The child has indicated that she feels comfortable talking to the practical nurse/nursing assistant. Suggesting she should talk to someone else may cause her to feel rejected and angry.

CLASSIFICATION

Competency Category:	Communication Skills
Taxonomic Level:	Application
Client Age:	Adult

REFERENCES

Jackson & Saunders (1993), p. 405
Whaley & Wong (1993), p. 519

85 CORRECT ANSWER: 3

1. At age 2, toddlers cannot dress themselves independently as they still need some help with fasteners.
2. Rather than dressing the client, the practical nurse/nursing assistant should encourage him to dress himself because this opportunity fosters autonomy.
3. The client should be encouraged to dress himself to foster autonomy. By age 2, toddlers are relatively independent with activities such as dressing.
4. Choice fosters autonomy for 2-year-olds, but the client should also be able to dress himself relatively independently.

CLASSIFICATION

Competency Category:	Client Care – Implementation
Taxonomic Level:	Application
Client Age:	Child & Adolescent

REFERENCES

Jackson & Saunders (1993), p. 283
Whaley & Wong (1993), p. 349

86 CORRECT ANSWER: 4

1. Directly approaching the co-worker may be considered as following the correct line of resolving a conflict of values. However, the issue requires consideration and resolution at a higher level.
2. The practical nurse/nursing assistant has a responsibility to safeguard clients when care is compromised by a co-worker or other person, and to maintain professional conduct. Considering the incident as acceptable behavior is inappropriate.
3. Discussing the incident further with the client may provide insight into what happened and the effects that the conduct has had on the client. However, collecting additional information does not resolve the basic issue.
4. Ethical issues often cannot be resolved as right or wrong; discussions with a superior can lead to actions that will resolve the issue.

CLASSIFICATION

Competency Category:	Professional and Personal Responsibilities
Taxonomic Level:	Critical Thinking
Client Age:	General

REFERENCES
Kozier et al. (1991), p. 132
Potter & Perry (1993), pp. 277, 282

87 CORRECT ANSWER: 3

1. Abdominal thrusts should be implemented for choking if the client cannot breathe, speak, or cough, as in a completely obstructed airway. The client is still able to cough, which means that his airway is only partially obstructed.
2. The obstruction is likely too deep to be effectively suctioned. There is a danger in changing the obstruction from partial to complete.
3. Because the obstruction is partial, as indicated by the client coughing, the practical nurse/nursing assistant should not interfere with the client's attempts to cough out the object.
4. The practical nurse/nursing assistant should call for assistance, but this situation does not necessitate an emergency code at this time.

CLASSIFICATION

Competency Category:	Client Care – Implementation
Taxonomic Level:	Application
Client Age:	Older Adult

REFERENCES
McCarthy et al. (1994), p. 63
Springhouse Corporation (1994), pp. 337–338

88 CORRECT ANSWER: 1

1. The agency's accepted protocol for a specific procedure is outlined and is considered the established practice for the practical nurse/nursing assistant to follow.
2. A procedural manual does not include every individual situation, and does not absolve the practical nurse/nursing assistant from client assessment responsibilities.
3. Equipment-related errors of misuse, disrepair, and malfunctioning are still a possibility, and the practical nurse's/nursing assistant's assessment responsibilities are required prior to and during equipment operation.
4. Sufficient instructions may not be provided, and the practical nurse/nursing assistant has the professional responsibility to seek verification and/or instruction if the equipment is unfamiliar and/or the procedure is unclear.

CLASSIFICATION

Competency Category: Professional and Personal Responsibilities

Taxonomic Level: Knowledge/Comprehension

Client Age: Adult

REFERENCES

McCarthy et al. (1994), p. 11

Potter & Perry (1993), p. 1439

89 CORRECT ANSWER: 3

1. Asking for information about his wife's medication does not reflect a recognition of the client's concern regarding his wife's safety.
2. Asking for information on the frequency of his wife's falls does not reflect a recognition of the client's concern regarding his wife's safety.
3. Replying accurately and specifically to the client's statement demonstrates that the practical nurse/nursing assistant is listening and reflecting the meaning that was being conveyed by the client.
4. Asking for information about care arrangements for his wife makes assumptions that were never expressed by the client.

CLASSIFICATION

Competency Category: Communication Skills

Taxonomic Level: Application

Client Age: Older Adult

REFERENCES

Long (1992), p. 58

Smith (1992), pp. 86–88

90 CORRECT ANSWER: 1

1. Arterial blood supplies warmth and oxygenated blood to the extremities. Therefore, a cyanotic and cold foot would most likely indicate arterial insufficiency due to occlusion.
2. Venous congestion results in edema, not arterial occlusion. The warmth indicates there is adequate arterial supply.
3. A dark red foot suggests congestion and a lack of venous return. The cool extremity may indicate an arterial disruption, but not in combination with congestion.
4. Dryness does not indicate a specific circulatory difficulty. In addition, the warmth indicates there is adequate arterial supply.

CLASSIFICATION

Competency Category: Client Care – Assessment
Taxonomic Level: Knowledge/Comprehension
Client Age: Older Adult

REFERENCES

Phipps et al. (1991), p. 739
Scherer (1991), p. 316

91 CORRECT ANSWER: 1

1. Establishing an appropriate schedule should help the toddler regain control.
2. Restricting fluid intake will decrease the amount of fluid in the bladder but will not contribute to bladder control.
3. Wearing training pants diminishes self-esteem and does not help to reestablish bladder control.
4. Withdrawing privileges is an inappropriate approach to take for a 3-year-old, who may not associate privilege withdrawal with her loss of bladder control.

CLASSIFICATION

Competency Category: Client Care – Implementation
Taxonomic Level: Application
Client Age: Child & Adolescent

REFERENCES

Pillitteri (1992), p. 903
Whaley & Wong (1993), p. 352

92 CORRECT ANSWER: 4

1. The code is in progress, therefore, oxygen and suction will already be in use.
2. Removing possible obstructions from the hallways is important before the team arrives.
3. It is inappropriate for the practical nurse/nursing assistant to leave the unit during an emergency.
4. It is the practical nurse's/nursing assistant's responsibility to ensure that clients receive competent care. It is appropriate for the practical nurse/nursing assistant to take over the care of other clients in an emergency.

CLASSIFICATION

Competency Category: Professional and Personal Responsibilities
Taxonomic Level: Application
Client Age: General

REFERENCES

Bolander (1994), p. 49
Yeo (1991), pp. 31–32

93 CORRECT ANSWER: 3

1. It is within the role of the practical nurse/nursing assistant to reinforce explanations, and it is necessary to ensure that the client's questions are addressed as soon as possible.
2. It is unethical for the practical nurse/nursing assistant to recommend a specific physician.
3. It is within the role of the practical nurse/nursing assistant to determine a client's level of understanding and clarify explanations provided by other members of the health care team.
4. The practical nurse/nursing assistant needs to first assess the client's level of understanding of earlier teaching. As well, it is inappropriate for the practical nurse/nursing assistant to introduce discussion of possible complications with the client.

CLASSIFICATION

Competency Category:	Professional and Personal Responsibilities
Taxonomic Level:	Application
Client Age:	General

REFERENCES

Christensen & Kockrow (1994), pp. 45–46, 62
Rosdahl (1991), pp. 291, 296

94 CORRECT ANSWER: 2

1. Eggnogs and milkshakes may not be the client's preferred foods.
2. Offering food supplements gives control to the client. It increases the likelihood of the food being consumed and should improve his nutritional status.
3. Promoting the consumption of small meals does not address the key concern of his nutritional status.
4. Not all high energy foods are nutritionally sound.

CLASSIFICATION

Competency Category:	Client Care – Implementation
Taxonomic Level:	Critical Thinking
Client Age:	Older Adult

REFERENCES

Poleman & Peckenpaugh (1991), pp. 259–260
Rosdahl (1991), p. 990

95 CORRECT ANSWER: 4

1. The client will be able to participate in most of his own bathing and should not be limited to helping the practical nurse/nursing assistant with face and hands only.
2. Drowning is a major cause of death for 3-year-olds. The client must be supervised at all times.
3. There is a potential for injury from burns as children at this age have great curiosity and are unaware of potential sources of burns. Therefore, the client should never be allowed to run his bathwater.
4. The practical nurse/nursing assistant must stay with the client at all times to maintain his safety. However, the client's autonomy and independence should be promoted by having him bathe himself.

CLASSIFICATION

Competency Category:	Client Care – Implementation
Taxonomic Level:	Application
Client Age:	Child & Adolescent

REFERENCES

Jackson & Saunders (1993), p. 283
Whaley & Wong (1993), pp. 358–359

96 CORRECT ANSWER: 1

1. Wearing gloves does not eliminate the need for, and should always be followed by, good handwashing. This is the best action to provide for medical asepsis when dealing with secretions.
2. There is no indication for double bagging tissues with secretions unless the client is in isolation.
3. Providing the client with the proper equipment is not as important a requirement of medical asepsis as handwashing.
4. If the client has a frequent cough, she will likely need a clean garbage bag more often than every 8 hours.

CLASSIFICATION

Competency Category:	Client Care – Implementation
Taxonomic Level:	Application
Client Age:	Adult

REFERENCES

Craven & Hirnle (1992), p. 440
Taylor et al. (1993), p. 512

97 CORRECT ANSWER: 4

1. The physician must adhere to the basic principle of confidentiality to protect the privacy of the client. It would not be appropriate for the practical nurse/nursing assistant to refer Sally to the physician.
2. The ordering of tests and the results are confidential and it would be inappropriate to discuss them with Sally.
3. Telling Sally to have an HIV test implies that Wade has been diagnosed as HIV-positive. This action is inappropriate because it breaches client confidentiality and possibly provides false information.
4. Suggesting that Sally talk directly to Wade may be the only way to resolve this dilemma, which involves professional ethics, legalities, and personal relationships. The client is the only person who can discuss this information with other people.

CLASSIFICATION

Competency Category:	Professional and Personal Responsibilities
Taxonomic Level:	Application
Client Age:	Child & Adolescent

REFERENCES

Craven & Hirnle (1992), p. 258
Potter & Perry (1993), pp. 276, 281

98 CORRECT ANSWER: 4

1. Offering to take the client to the shower in a shower-chair is inappropriate because the practical nurse/nursing assistant does not know her needs or preferences.
2. Assisting the client to the sink to bathe may not be appropriate as it may not address her needs or preferences.
3. The client may require more assistance than just being provided with the necessary supplies.
4. The amount of assistance needed with bathing is a nursing decision that includes consideration of the benefits, safety, and personal preferences of the client.

CLASSIFICATION

Competency Category:	Client Care – Implementation
Taxonomic Level:	Application
Client Age:	Child & Adolescent

REFERENCES

Bolander (1994), p. 916
Rosdahl (1991), p. 345

99 CORRECT ANSWER: 2

1. The client may respond even if the practical nurse/nursing assistant calls him by the wrong name.
2. Asking the client what his name is should safely verify his identity.
3. The client may be in a different room from that indicated on the card on the special diet tray.
4. Gaining the assistance of another client may not be an accurate way to verify the client's identity.

CLASSIFICATION

Competency Category: Client Care – Implementation
Taxonomic Level: Knowledge/Comprehension
Client Age: Child & Adolescent

REFERENCES

Taylor et al. (1993), p. 1203
Timby & Lewis (1992), p. 227

100 CORRECT ANSWER: 3

1. Washing from the groin towards the glans penis does not follow the principles of medical asepsis, because it increases the risk of microorganisms entering the urethral meatus.
2. Washing the glans penis after the shaft does not follow the principles of medical asepsis, because it increases the risk of microorganisms entering the urethral meatus.
3. The correct sequence provides for medical asepsis by washing microorganisms away from the urethral meatus and making contamination less likely.
4. Washing the glans penis after the scrotum and the penile shaft does not follow the principles of medical asepsis, because it increases the chance of contamination.

CLASSIFICATION

Competency Category: Client Care – Implementation
Taxonomic Level: Knowledge/Comprehension
Client Age: Adult

REFERENCES

Potter & Perry (1991), p. 684
Timby & Lewis (1992), p. 97

101 CORRECT ANSWER: 4

1. It may be inappropriate to place a call bell near the client's dominant hand, because she has left hemiparesis and may be left-handed.
2. It would be inappropriate to put a call bell on the client's left side, because she has a left hemiparesis.
3. The call bell should not be attached to the side rail, because there is no guarantee that the client would be able to reach it.
4. The call bell should be on the right side, as the client's right side is functional.

CLASSIFICATION

Competency Category: Client Care – Implementation
Taxonomic Level: Application
Client Age: Older Adult

REFERENCES

deWit & Keane (1992), pp. 342–343
Sorrentino (1992), p. 176

102 CORRECT ANSWER: 2

1. The practical nurse/nursing assistant should follow up this statement by looking for a foot injury, but this information would not need to be reported immediately.
2. "Feeling funny" is a symptom of hypoglycemia and must be reported immediately.
3. The practical nurse/nursing assistant needs to gather more information before acting on this statement. Preschoolers often have fears and imagine monsters.
4. The practical nurse/nursing assistant needs to gather more information before acting on this statement. It is not unusual for children to say they hate the person they view as responsible for their hospitalization.

CLASSIFICATION

Competency Category:	Client Care – Assessment
Taxonomic Level:	Application
Client Age:	Child & Adolescent

REFERENCES

Rosdahl (1991), p. 951
Whaley & Wong (1993), p. 1004

103 CORRECT ANSWER: 3

1. Libel is a written statement that conveys an unfavorable impression.
2. This situation describes a breach of ethics as it deals with moral behavior. However, breach of confidentiality is a more specific term to use.
3. Breach of confidentiality is the violation of another person's right to privacy and is one type of nonethical behavior.
4. Verbal assault is a deliberate attempt to hurt another person. The health care workers did not necessarily mean to harm the client or his character.

CLASSIFICATION

Competency Category:	Professional and Personal Responsibilities
Taxonomic Level:	Knowledge/Comprehension
Client Age:	General

REFERENCES

Potter & Perry (1993), p. 281
Wilson & Kneisl (1992), p. 123

CHAPTER 7

CASE 8

1 CORRECT ANSWER: 3

1. Showing disagreement with the client's statement is judgmental and may alter communications, which may hinder the assessment of the client's needs. In addition, the practical nurse/nursing assistant is belittling the client's concerns.
2. This response is not appropriate because giving an opinion distracts the client from determining his own needs. As well, offering false reassurances is misleading and/or unrealistic.
3. This response is the most appropriate because the practical nurse/nursing assistant is encouraging the client to express his feelings.
4. This response is not appropriate because offering false reassurances is misleading and/or unrealistic.

CLASSIFICATION

Competency Category: Client Care – Assessment
Taxonomic Level: Affective
Client Age: Adult

REFERENCES
Potter & Perry (1991), p. 184
Smith (1992), p. 28

2 CORRECT ANSWER: 2

1. This intervention considers physical needs rather than emotional support.
2. Touching the client's shoulder conveys emotional support and acceptance.
3. This intervention avoids direct physical contact with the client and may convey a message of avoidance.
4. This intervention is invasive and, rather than providing emotional support, may cause alienation with the client.

CLASSIFICATION

Competency Category: Communication Skills
Taxonomic Level: Application
Client Age: Adult

REFERENCES
Potter & Perry (1991), p. 176
Smith (1992), p. 59

3 CORRECT ANSWER: 3

1. This diet promotes tissue growth and repair, but the low kilojoule (Calorie) will not meet his increased metabolic needs.
2. The low protein diet would not meet the need for tissue growth and repair.
3. This diet promotes tissue growth, tissue repair, and increased metabolic needs for healing.
4. This diet does not promote tissue growth, repair, or maintenance.

CLASSIFICATION

Competency Category:	Client Care – Implementation
Taxonomic Level:	Application
Client Age:	Adult

REFERENCES

Smeltzer & Bare (1992), p. 1526
Sorrentino (1992), p. 269

4 CORRECT ANSWER: 4

1. Selecting the appropriate teaching aids is an appropriate intervention, but it is not the initial intervention.
2. Determining Mr. Henry's level of knowledge is an appropriate intervention, but it is not the initial intervention.
3. Researching the material is an appropriate intervention, but it is not the initial intervention.
4. Learning will not occur unless the client is ready to learn.

CLASSIFICATION

Competency Category:	Client Care – Implementation
Taxonomic Level:	Knowledge/Comprehension
Client Age:	Adult

REFERENCES

Potter & Perry (1993), p. 367
Smeltzer & Bare (1992), p. 43

5 CORRECT ANSWER: 1

1. Frequent seepage of watery stool is a manifestation of fecal impaction as liquid feces pass around the hardened stool.
2. Small, hard, and dry stool is a sign of constipation as the feces move slowly through the intestine allowing more time for the absorption of water.
3. Nausea and vomiting are rarely associated with fecal impaction.
4. Black tarry stool is not a sign of fecal impaction. It usually indicates a disease process or the ingestion of iron.

CLASSIFICATION

Competency Category:	Client Care – Assessment
Taxonomic Level:	Application
Client Age:	Adult

REFERENCES

Potter & Perry (1991), p. 796
Sorrentino (1992), p. 253

CORRECT ANSWER: 1

1. The responsibility of informing the client rests with the physician, and it is the role of the nurse-in-charge to notify the physician.
2. This action is not within the legal parameters of the practical nurse/nursing assistant. The practical nurse/nursing assistant may reinforce the purpose of surgery, but would not explain it initially.
3. This action is not valid as it violates the client's right to informed consent.
4. This action is not appropriate because there is no indication that the surgery needs to be cancelled, but there is a need to obtain an informed consent.

CLASSIFICATION

Competency Category:	Professional and Personal Responsibilities
Taxonomic Level:	Application
Client Age:	Adult

REFERENCES
Bolander (1994), p. 706
Sorrentino (1992), p. 21

CASE 9

 CORRECT ANSWER: 4

1. Midstream urine requires a specimen midway through the stream of urine.
2. Midstream urine requires a specimen midway through the stream of urine. In addition, a container with a preservative is not necessary for a specimen of urine for culture and sensitivity.
3. The collection container must be sterile to ensure that only bacteria in the urine may grow during the test.
4. Voiding in this manner will provide a specimen midway through the stream of urine. In addition, a sterile container is free of any bacteria.

CLASSIFICATION

Competency Category:	Client Care – Implementation
Taxonomic Level:	Knowledge/Comprehension
Client Age:	Older Adult

REFERENCES
McCarthy et al. (1994), p. 204
Rosdahl (1991), p. 684

8 CORRECT ANSWER: 3

1. Scrubbing the skin is contraindicated as this action may lead to skin breakdown. In addition, the use of antiseptic soap is not necessary.
2. The use of hot water is contraindicated as this temperature may cause burning to the perineum.
3. This intervention promotes safe skin care and principles of medical asepsis.
4. This intervention is contraindicated as cleansing other than in a downward direction, away from the meatus, may introduce bacteria into the bladder.

CLASSIFICATION

Competency Category:	Client Care – Implementation
Taxonomic Level:	Knowledge/Comprehension
Client Age:	Older Adult

REFERENCES
McCarthy et al. (1994), p. 199
Potter & Perry (1993), p. 1372

9 CORRECT ANSWER: 2

1. This intervention disrupts urinary flow because the drainage bag is higher than bladder position.
2. This intervention maintains urinary drainage because the drainage bag is lower than bladder position.
3. This intervention disrupts the flow of urine by gravity. In addition, the drainage bag is likely higher than bladder position.
4. This intervention disrupts the flow of urine by gravity.

CLASSIFICATION

Competency Category:	Client Care – Implementation
Taxonomic Level:	Application
Client Age:	Older Adult

REFERENCES

deWit (1994), p. 647
Sorrentino (1992), p. 235

10 CORRECT ANSWER: 4

1. Meeting the need of increased fluids is a nursing responsibility, not the food service's responsibility.
2. It is not the family's responsibility to see that this need is met.
3. This action would ensure fluid availability, but not adequate nutrition. In addition, the client would likely not be on a clear liquid diet.
4. Fluids offered at regular, frequent intervals should increase daily fluid intake.

CLASSIFICATION

Competency Category:	Client Care – Implementation
Taxonomic Level:	Application
Client Age:	Older Adult

REFERENCES

Christensen & Kockrow (1994), p. 506
Sorrentino (1992), pp. 275–276

11 CORRECT ANSWER: 4

1. This intervention promotes adequate fluid intake, not necessarily bladder retraining.
2. n.p.o. is not indicated for this client.
3. This observation indicates urinary retention rather than promoting bladder retraining.
4. Scheduled times of voiding promote bladder muscle control.

CLASSIFICATION

Competency Category:	Client Care – Implementation
Taxonomic Level:	Application
Client Age:	Older Adult

REFERENCES

Potter & Perry (1991), p. 776
Sorrentino (1992), p. 239

CASE 10

12 CORRECT ANSWER: 3

1. Speaking rapidly and wringing hands usually indicate nervousness rather than pain.
2. Refusing to make eye contact and crying easily are typically associated with depression, not specifically pain.
3. The client in pain tends to try to move very little to avoid pain. Pain is often observed through facial expression.
4. Cuddling her doll and referring to it as her "baby" is likely indicating that the client is comfortable and not in pain.

CLASSIFICATION

Competency Category: Client Care – Assessment
Taxonomic Level: Knowledge/Comprehension
Client Age: Older Adult

REFERENCES
Black & Matassarin-Jacobs (1993), pp. 318–319
Bolander (1994), p. 975

13 CORRECT ANSWER: 4

1. Bathing the client twice a day will promote skin breakdown. In addition, medicated soap is not indicated in the prevention of decubitus ulcers.
2. The use of bath oil will not prevent the formation of decubitus ulcers, regardless of the number of times per day it is used. In addition, bathing the elderly daily is not advised.
3. It is contraindicated to massage reddened bony areas because it may promote skin breakdown.
4. The client should be assisted or encouraged to turn every 2 hours to reduce the likelihood of decubitus ulcer formation, because it reduces the extended pressure on vulnerable areas.

CLASSIFICATION

Competency Category: Client Care – Implementation
Taxonomic Level: Application
Client Age: Older Adult

REFERENCES
Bolander (1994), pp. 1345–1350
Walston & Walston (1995), pp. 224–226

14 CORRECT ANSWER: 3

1. This statement negates the client's feelings and does not give her a chance to discuss her concerns.
2. In this instance, the practical nurse/nursing assistant is avoiding dealing with the problem at hand by leaving the room.
3. This approach shows empathy, warmth, and interest in the client and her concerns, and opens an opportunity for discussion.
4. This statement passes the problem on to someone else, when it could be dealt with at this time by the practical nurse/nursing assistant, using appropriate communication skills.

CLASSIFICATION

Competency Category: Communication Skills
Taxonomic Level: Affective
Client Age: Older Adult

REFERENCES
Potter & Perry (1991), pp. 626–633
Walston & Walston (1995), pp. 132–134

15 CORRECT ANSWER: 2

1. Tomato juice is the only liquid item in this group of foods. Green beans and mashed potatoes would not be listed on the intake and output sheet.
2. These items are all liquids and, therefore, can all be recorded on the intake and output sheet.
3. Toast is not considered a liquid intake.
4. Beef stew and canned peaches would not be listed on the intake and output sheet.

CLASSIFICATION

Competency Category: Client Care – Assessment
Taxonomic Level: Knowledge/Comprehension
Client Age: Older Adult

REFERENCES

Kozier et al. (1991), p. 1055
Walston & Walston (1995), pp. 98–100

CASE 11

16 CORRECT ANSWER: 1

1. The practical nurse/nursing assistant has a responsibility to remind co-workers that conversations taking place in the coffee lounge can be overheard by others.
2. While this might seem like an appropriate action, it does nothing to address the immediate problem and may only upset the client.
3. Reporting the incident to the nurse-in-charge should occur only if co-workers fail to adhere to confidentiality guidelines in the future.
4. Suggesting an inservice program might be a good idea should the problem continue, but it does not deal with the immediate problem.

CLASSIFICATION

Competency Category: Professional and Personal
                                     Responsibilities
Taxonomic Level: Affective
Client Age: Adult

REFERENCES

Beare & Myers (1990), pp. 126–130
Yeo (1991), pp. 120–123

17 CORRECT ANSWER: 1

1. Reddened tissue is an early sign of a potential for skin breakdown.
2. Numbness is a later manifestation of skin breakdown.
3. With a broken blister, the damage has already taken place.
4. Excoriation indicates that skin breakdown has already occurred.

CLASSIFICATION

Competency Category: Client Care – Assessment
Taxonomic Level: Knowledge/Comprehension
Client Age: Adult

REFERENCES
Durham & Cohen (1991), p. 219
Sorrentino (1992), p. 202

18 CORRECT ANSWER: 3

1. The client should be encouraged to be as mobile as possible.
2. Massage of reddened areas would promote further breakdown.
3. Clients should be repositioned every 2 hours to prevent further breakdown.
4. A compress is not required in this situation because there is no evidence of skin breakdown.

CLASSIFICATION

Competency Category: Client Care – Implementation
Taxonomic Level: Application
Client Age: Adult

REFERENCES
Durham & Cohen (1991), p. 219
Sorrentino (1992), p. 227

19 CORRECT ANSWER: 3

1. The practical nurse/nursing assistant should monitor the number of visitors. Too many visitors would not promote relaxation and sleep for a client who is exhausted.
2. Monitoring outgoing calls does not respect the rights of the client and does not promote relaxation and sleep.
3. Reorganizing the client's nursing care will minimize interruptions and provide a restful environment.
4. Sleep medication should be recommended only after other methods have been tried.

CLASSIFICATION

Competency Category: Client Care – Implementation
Taxonomic Level: Application
Client Age: Adult

REFERENCES
Durham & Cohen (1991), p. 209
Timby & Lewis (1992), pp. 192–193

20 CORRECT ANSWER: 1

1. Edema and pallor at the I.V. insertion site would indicate that infiltration has taken place.
2. Redness and pain at the I.V. site are manifestations of phlebitis, not infiltration.
3. Pallor occurs with I.V. infiltration, but the flow rate usually decreases.
4. Although there may be leakage at the site, redness should not occur.

CLASSIFICATION

Competency Category:	Client Care – Assessment
Taxonomic Level:	Critical Thinking
Client Age:	Adult

REFERENCES
Perry & Potter (1994), pp. 604–610
Suddarth (1991), pp. 85–86

21 CORRECT ANSWER: 1

1. A conversion chart provides the client with an easy and accurate conversion method for recording intake.
2. Reminding the client to drink plenty of fluids does not address the need to record intake and output.
3. Recording I.V. therapy is not the responsibility of the client, who would have no idea of the I.V. therapy he has received.
4. Pureed foods are not considered a fluid and, therefore, would not be included when recording fluid intake.

CLASSIFICATION

Competency Category:	Client Care – Assessment
Taxonomic Level:	Application
Client Age:	Adult

REFERENCES
Perry & Potter (1994), p. 732
Sorrentino (1992), p. 278

CASE 12

22 CORRECT ANSWER: 1

1. Orienting the client to the unit decreases anxiety and is within the scope of practice of a practical nurse/nursing assistant.
2. Notifying the family physician is the responsibility of the registered nurse.
3. Testing a blood specimen is the responsibility of the lab technician.
4. Ensuring bedrest is not a component of the admission procedure unless an order has been written.

CLASSIFICATION

Competency Category:	Client Care – Implementation
Taxonomic Level:	Knowledge/Comprehension
Client Age:	Adult

REFERENCES
Kozier et al. (1993), p. 110
Potter & Perry (1993), p. 124

23 CORRECT ANSWER: 4

1. Independent mobility does not indicate a problem.
2. A food allergy is not an immediate concern.
3. A blood pressure of 120/80 mmHg is normal for a 25-year-old female.
4. Numbess is the client's immediate problem. Dealing with it first indicates that the practical nurse/nursing assistant is concerned with the client's welfare. It also helps to initiate a sense of security and a trusting relationship.

CLASSIFICATION

Competency Category:	Client Care – Assessment
Taxonomic Level:	Critical Thinking
Client Age:	Adult

REFERENCES

Kozier et al. (1993), p. 110
Potter & Perry (1993), p. 124

24 CORRECT ANSWER: 4

1. Crossing arms is a defensive position and does not encourage communication.
2. Minimizing eye contact may indicate to the client that the practical nurse/nursing assistant is unwilling to listen to her.
3. Writing should be kept to a minimum when listening to a client.
4. An open posture indicates that the listener wants to encourage communication.

CLASSIFICATION

Competency Category:	Communication Skills
Taxonomic Level:	Affective
Client Age:	Adult

REFERENCES

Kozier et al. (1993), p. 71
Potter & Perry (1993), p. 320

25 CORRECT ANSWER: 1

1. Encouraging the performance of prescribed exercises is within the scope of practice of the practical nurse/nursing assistant.
2. Passive exercises do not produce the same results as active exercises.
3. The exercises must not be changed without consultation with the physiotherapist.
4. Exercises should not cause pain.

CLASSIFICATION

Competency Category:	Client Care – Implementation
Taxonomic Level:	Knowledge/Comprehension
Client Age:	Adult

REFERENCES

Potter & Perry (1993), pp. 200–201
Sorrentino (1992), p. 390

26 CORRECT ANSWER: 3

1. A prone position should be avoided by people who have back problems.
2. Staying in the same position will precipitate the complications associated with immobility.
3. Previously successful pain management techniques often work best. It may comfort the client to know that the practical nurse/nursing assistant is willing to use the client's relief measures.
4. A lumbosacral brace requires a physician's order and is not recommended for long-term use, because it restricts movement and causes further weakening of the back muscles.

CLASSIFICATION

Competency Category:	Client Care – Planning
Taxonomic Level:	Knowledge/Comprehension
Client Age:	Adult

REFERENCES

Christensen & Kockrow (1994), pp. 259–260
Potter & Perry (1993), pp. 1190–1191

27 CORRECT ANSWER: 2

1. The knees should be kept level with the hips when sitting.
2. When lifting, twisting at the waist puts stress on the back.
3. When bending, a wide base of support is required.
4. Clients with back problems should be supported in a straight-backed chair, not with pillows.

CLASSIFICATION

Competency Category:	Client Care – Implementation
Taxonomic Level:	Application
Client Age:	Adult

REFERENCES

Beare & Myers (1990), p. 1377
Suddarth (1991), pp. 803–804

CASE 13

28 CORRECT ANSWER: 1

1. Regular check of flow meter rate ensures the delivery of prescribed oxygen concentration.
2. Lubrication with water could result in choking caused by inhaled moisture.
3. Maintaining the water level ensures adequate humidification of oxygen, but sterile water should be used.
4. A tight fit for the headband can result in tissue damage over the ears and against the nares because of the excessive pressure.

CLASSIFICATION

Competency Category:	Client Care – Implementation
Taxonomic Level:	Application
Client Age:	Older Adult

REFERENCES

Kozier et al. (1993), p. 786
Perry & Potter (1993), pp. 352–353

29 CORRECT ANSWER: 3

1. Chest pain is a subjective manifestation that may be related to dyspnea.
2. Dizziness is a subjective manifestation that may be related to dyspnea.
3. Intercostal muscle use is the singular objective manifestation of dyspnea.
4. Increased thirst is a subjective manifestation and has little, if any, bearing on dyspnea.

CLASSIFICATION

Competency Category: Client Care – Assessment
Taxonomic Level: Knowledge/Comprehension
Client Age: Older Adult

REFERENCES

Black & Matassarin-Jacobs (1993), p. 914
Potter & Perry (1993), p. 488

30 CORRECT ANSWER: 1

1. Sharp, left-sided chest pain is a precise description of the nature and location of the pain.
2. Difficulty with breathing at mealtime is a subjective, not objective, description.
3. Pain when getting out of bed describes the time of the pain but gives no clues about the nature of the pain.
4. The location of the dryness caused by the nasal cannula is not specified.

CLASSIFICATION

Competency Category: Communication Skills
Taxonomic Level: Application
Client Age: Older Adult

REFERENCES

Potter & Perry (1993), p. 697
Smith (1992), p. 89

31 CORRECT ANSWER: 1

1. This response enhances further communication and leaves the direction of the interaction up to the client.
2. This response blocks further communication by belittling the client's concerns.
3. This statement is a superficial attempt at reassurance that does nothing to address the client's fear of dying.
4. This statement indicates that the practical nurse/nursing assistant has not really heard the client's statement. "Why" questions tend to be threatening and to block communication.

CLASSIFICATION

Competency Category: Communication Skills
Taxonomic Level: Critical Thinking
Client Age: Older Adult

REFERENCES

Hill (1993), pp. 166–170
Potter & Perry (1993), pp. 321–325

32 CORRECT ANSWER: 4

1. Side-lying with the limbs supported promotes comfort and respirations but it is not the best position for a client with dyspnea.
2. Semi-Fowler's position would not enhance breathing adequately for a client with dyspnea.
3. A dorsal recumbent position would aggravate the dyspnea.
4. High-Fowler's with arms supported enhances breathing by facilitating the expansion of the client's chest and enhancing oxygenation, thereby increasing comfort.

CLASSIFICATION

Competency Category:	Client Care – Implementation
Taxonomic Level:	Application
Client Age:	Older Adult

REFERENCES

Potter & Perry (1993), pp. 1491–1494
Timby & Lewis (1992), pp. 396–399

33 CORRECT ANSWER: 1

1. Avoiding contact with infections of the upper respiratory tract is advised for chronic obstructive pulmonary disease (COPD).
2. Elastic stockings are not an intervention for COPD.
3. Fluids should be increased rather than decreased in COPD to liquefy secretions.
4. Increasing the oxygen flow rate is not advised for clients with COPD because their drive to breathe is regulated by their blood oxygen level.

CLASSIFICATION

Competency Category:	Client Care – Implementation
Taxonomic Level:	Critical Thinking
Client Age:	Older Adult

REFERENCES

Hood & Dincher (1992), p. 329
Smeltzer & Bare (1992), p. 580

CASE 14

34 CORRECT ANSWER: 2

1. Blood pressure decreases with a decreased amount of volume.
2. Blood pressure tends to be lowest in the morning and highest later in the day.
3. Syncope occurs with low blood pressure and insufficient blood supply to the brain.
4. Blood pressure tends to increase with age.

CLASSIFICATION

Competency Category:	Client Care – Assessment
Taxonomic Level:	Knowledge/Comprehension
Client Age:	Older Adult

REFERENCES

Potter & Perry (1993), p. 490
Timby & Lewis (1992), p. 260

35 CORRECT ANSWER: 3

1. An electrocardiogram is a noninvasive cardiac procedure and, therefore, no internal bleeding will occur.
2. There is no puncture site with an electrocardiogram.
3. Anxiety may be high with a test situation. The assessment of anxiety is particularly important with cardiac clients.
4. Pedal pulses are not affected by an electrocardiogram.

CLASSIFICATION

Competency Category:	Client Care – Assessment
Taxonomic Level:	Application
Client Age:	Older Adult

REFERENCES

Black & Matassarin-Jacobs (1993), p. 1171
Potter & Perry (1993), p. 1239

36 CORRECT ANSWER: 4

1. The use of lotion is contraindicated because of the risk of growth of microorganisms.
2. The catheter bag should be below waist level to permit proper urinary drainage.
3. Fluids should be increased to create a natural flushing of the urinary tract.
4. The fact that the client removes the encrusted material demonstrates an understanding. The collection of material at the meatus may lead to urethral irritation and infection.

CLASSIFICATION

Competency Category:	Client Care – Implementation
Taxonomic Level:	Application
Client Age:	Older Adult

REFERENCES

Hood & Dincher (1992), pp. 506–509
Perry & Potter (1994), pp. 745–748

37 CORRECT ANSWER: 3

1. Fluids should be consumed between meals to prevent the client from becoming extremely thirsty.
2. Clients should be provided with small containers of fluids at frequent intervals to decrease the desire for more fluids.
3. Ice chips are a good alternative because they take longer to melt. In addition, fluid intake is calculated as half of the frozen volume.
4. Over-emphasizing may discourage the client and may result in frustration.

CLASSIFICATION

Competency Category:	Client Care – Implementation
Taxonomic Level:	Application
Client Age:	Older Adult

REFERENCES

Kozier et al. (1991), p. 1063
Potter & Perry (1993), p. 1303

38 CORRECT ANSWER: 4

1. Elastic support stockings require a physician's order. In addition, they provide care for venous congestion, not feet.
2. Hot foot soaks are not recommended for a client with a potential for decreased circulation.
3. Correctly fitting shoes are recommended at all times, and are particularly important given the client's condition and age.
4. Daily assessment will help detect changes before problems occur.

CLASSIFICATION

Competency Category:	Client Care – Implementation
Taxonomic Level:	Application
Client Age:	Older Adult

REFERENCES
Kozier et al. (1991), p. 527
Potter & Perry (1993), p. 1045

39 CORRECT ANSWER: 4

1. Reviewing the risk factors does not focus specifically on those risk factors pertinent to Mr. Snow.
2. Identifying changes does not describe the reason for quitting; it may scare the client, and it does not emphasize the positive effects of quitting.
3. Creating a schedule is helpful, but it does not help the client to understand the reason for quitting.
4. Explaining the effects of smoking on the heart by using a visual aid would be most effective.

CLASSIFICATION

Competency Category:	Client Care – Implementation
Taxonomic Level:	Application
Client Age:	Older Adult

REFERENCES
Kozier et al. (1991), p. 1098
Potter & Perry (1993), p. 1229

INDEPENDENT QUESTIONS

40 CORRECT ANSWER: 4

1. Asking the clients about the pills is unsafe practice and does not address the initial problem of client safety.
2. As safety of any client is a priority for the practical nurse/nursing assistant, leaving the pills in the bathroom violates this responsibility.
3. Disposing of the pills down the toilet will not help to identify which client has not taken prescribed pills.
4. Giving the pills to the nurse-in-charge may permit possible identification of the owner of the pills. Also, reporting of the incident is correct practice.

CLASSIFICATION

Competency Category: Communication Skills
Taxonomic Level: Application
Client Age: General

REFERENCES

Kozier et al. (1991), p. 315
Potter & Perry (1993), p. 700

41 CORRECT ANSWER: 1

1. The goal of universal precautions is to treat every client as if infectious. The wearing of disposable gloves prevents cross-contamination. Blood and body fluids are two of the main vectors for transmission of many diseases.
2. Disposable gloves are not a substitute for handwashing. Hands are washed immediately before applying gloves and immediately after removing them.
3. Maintaining sterility is not an objective for perineal care, because it is a clean procedure. In addition, the gloves do not have to be sterile.
4. Although disposable gloves should be worn to protect the client from infection, it is important to prevent cross-contamination.

CLASSIFICATION

Competency Category: Client Care – Implementation
Taxonomic Level: Application
Client Age: General

REFERENCES

Black & Matassarin-Jacobs (1993), p. 553
Potter & Perry (1991), pp. 522–523

42 CORRECT ANSWER: 1

1. Familiar toys help toddlers adjust to new or unfamiliar surroundings by giving them some feelings of security and an association with the familiar.
2. A toy, whether a favorite or not, will not necessarily provide a diversion or keep the toddler quiet.
3. A favorite toy does not guarantee socialization.
4. A favorite toy will not necessarily ensure participation in other play activities.

CLASSIFICATION

Competency Category:	Client Care – Assessment
Taxonomic Level:	Application
Client Age:	Child & Adolescent

REFERENCES

Jackson & Saunders (1993), pp. 133–134
Whaley & Wong (1991), pp. 650–651

43 CORRECT ANSWER: 2

1. The side-lying position is appropriate, but it is not the initial intervention in this situation.
2. A physician's order is required to give an enema. Therefore, the initial intervention the practical nurse/nursing assistant should implement is to check the physician's order.
3. Providing privacy is part of the procedure, but it is not the initial intervention.
4. This intervention would be appropriate prior to administering the enema, but it is not the initial intervention.

CLASSIFICATION

Competency Category:	Client Care – Implementation
Taxonomic Level:	Knowledge/Comprehension
Client Age:	General

REFERENCES

Rosdahl (1991), p. 358
Sorrentino (1992), p. 254

44 CORRECT ANSWER: 1

1. Checking the sling and straps should be the first safety check before any equipment is used.
2. Positioning the top of the sling under Mr. Jones's shoulders is part of the transfer procedure, but the straps would need to be checked first.
3. While folding Mr. Jones's arms across his chest needs to be done, it should take place after the equipment is checked.
4. Ensuring that the bed is in the lowest position and that the head is raised would only be done after the sling has been positioned.

CLASSIFICATION

Competency Category:	Client Care – Implementation
Taxonomic Level:	Application
Client Age:	Older Adult

REFERENCES

Kozier et al. (1993), p. 475
Sorrentino (1992), p. 164

45 CORRECT ANSWER: 3

1. This positioning aide will not prevent abduction of the legs, as it only keeps the bed linen off the feet.
2. The use of sandbags between the legs will help prevent adduction of the legs, not abduction.
3. Trochanter rolls placed bilaterally will prevent the legs from abducting.
4. The footboard will not prevent abduction of the legs.

CLASSIFICATION

Competency Category:	Client Care – Implementation
Taxonomic Level:	Application
Client Age:	Child & Adolescent

REFERENCES
deWit (1994), p. 122
Suddarth (1991), p. 133

46 CORRECT ANSWER: 2

1. This is an appropriate action, but not the initial action to take.
2. Giving away personal possessions, an unusual behavior, may be an indication of suicidal thoughts and must be immediately reported to the nurse-in-charge.
3. Reporting the information to the mother is not the action that should be taken initially.
4. This action ignores the possibility of immediate danger to the client who may be experiencing suicidal thoughts.

CLASSIFICATION

Competency Category:	Professional and Personal Responsibilities
Taxonomic Level:	Application
Client Age:	Child & Adolescent

REFERENCES
Rosdahl (1991), p. 678
Whaley & Wong (1991), p. 983

47 CORRECT ANSWER: 3

1. Involvement of the physician should not be requested until further assessment of the reasons for noncompliance has been completed.
2. Involvement of the dietitian should not be requested until further assessment of the reasons for noncompliance has been completed.
3. Setting nursing care goals needs to begin with adequate input from the client, who is a partner in the process.
4. Allowing the consequences of behavior to be experienced can be useful but, in this case, the consequences could be too threatening to the client's well-being.

CLASSIFICATION

Competency Category:	Client Care – Planning
Taxonomic Level:	Critical Thinking
Client Age:	Child & Adolescent

REFERENCES
deWit & Keane (1992), p. 49
Potter & Perry (1993), p. 148

48 CORRECT ANSWER: 4

1. Medical asepsis does not require the use of sterile gloves.
2. Nonsterile gloves are not necessary because there is no break in the skin integrity.
3. Medical asepsis does not require the use of sterile forceps.
4. Medical asepsis requires that the practical nurse/nursing assistant have clean hands prior to applying compresses to intact integument.

CLASSIFICATION

Competency Category: Client Care – Implementation
Taxonomic Level: Knowledge/Comprehension
Client Age: Child & Adolescent

REFERENCES
deWit (1994), pp. 84–88
Rosdahl (1991), pp. 453, 721

49 CORRECT ANSWER: 3

1. The client may not be capable of providing this information.
2. This statement assumes the client's identity without verification.
3. This approach verifies the client identity.
4. This approach assumes the client can accurately identify herself.

CLASSIFICATION

Competency Category: Client Care – Implementation
Taxonomic Level: Application
Client Age: General

REFERENCES
deWit (1994), pp. 872–873
Rosdahl (1991), pp. 309, 486

50 CORRECT ANSWER: 1

1. Taking Bobby to the playroom would give him the opportunity to interact with the other children and parents, and is a measure that the practical nurse/nursing assistant could initiate immediately.
2. Encouraging Bobby's family to visit does not ensure an increase in his social interaction.
3. Homework is a good idea, but does not ensure an opportunity for social interaction because it is a diversionary activity.
4. While having Bobby watch television would be a distraction, it would not increase the opportunity for him to interact socially.

CLASSIFICATION

Competency Category: Communication Skills
Taxonomic Level: Application
Client Age: Child & Adolescent

REFERENCES
Jackson & Saunders (1993), pp. 532–533
Whaley & Wong (1993), pp. 610–611

51 CORRECT ANSWER: 3

1. It is the surgeon's responsibility to inform the client of the risks of surgery.
2. It is the responsibility of the registered nurse giving the medication to explain the effects to the client.
3. If the client knows beforehand what he will be expected to do and what special equipment will be required, he is more likely to accept these postoperatively.
4. The routine practice is to have the client void before preoperative medication is administered, so that the medication will have the maximum benefit of relaxing the client, as well as promoting client safety due to side effects of lightheadedness and drowsiness.

CLASSIFICATION

Competency Category:	Client Care – Implementation
Taxonomic Level:	Knowledge/Comprehension
Client Age:	Older Adult

REFERENCES
Hood & Dincher (1992), p. 103
Smeltzer & Bare (1992), p. 410

52 CORRECT ANSWER: 4

1. This statement assumes that a time limitation is the problem.
2. This is a demanding type of statement and does not allow the client to make an independent decision.
3. This statement does not promote independence and may not make the client feel better.
4. This statement allows the client to make the decision of which item he will put on and the amount of assistance required.

CLASSIFICATION

Competency Category:	Client Care – Implementation
Taxonomic Level:	Critical Thinking
Client Age:	Adult

REFERENCES
Potter & Perry (1993), p. 824
Timby & Lewis (1992), p. 29

53 CORRECT ANSWER: 2

1. This statement offers an inappropriate alternative rather than encouragement to have the procedure.
2. This statement shows acceptance of the client's concern and also provides a practical explanation for helping her make an informed decision.
3. This statement is judgmental, placing blame on the client. It does not help her make an informed decision.
4. This statement belittles the client's concern. There is no attempt to help her make an informed decision.

CLASSIFICATION

Competency Category:	Communication Skills
Taxonomic Level:	Affective
Client Age:	General

REFERENCES
Smith (1992), pp. 28–29
Sorrentino (1992), p. 45

54 CORRECT ANSWER: 4

1. The client is aphasic. Therefore, she is unable to communicate verbally.
2. Although this approach could be used to validate the client's abilities, it is not the best method of assessment.
3. The client was previously at home and not in the hospital.
4. The client's husband has been caring for her. Therefore, he is the most reliable source of information.

CLASSIFICATION

Competency Category:	Client Care – Assessment
Taxonomic Level:	Application
Client Age:	Adult

REFERENCES

Rosdahl (1991), p. 1006
Suddarth (1991), p. 120

55 CORRECT ANSWER: 3

1. This response assumes that the problem is pain and does not seek to find the real problem.
2. This response is inappropriate because it minimizes the client's concerns by not addressing them.
3. This response encourages the client to openly discuss her feelings about the dressing change.
4. This response does not acknowledge that the problem can be corrected; rather, it merely indicates that the practical nurse/nursing assistant needs the time. It does not involve the client in decision making regarding her dressing change.

CLASSIFICATION

Competency Category:	Client Care – Evaluation
Taxonomic Level:	Affective
Client Age:	General

REFERENCES

Potter & Perry (1993), pp. 330–331
Timby & Lewis (1992), p. 23

56 CORRECT ANSWER: 1

1. Passive exercises maintain joint flexibility.
2. This response does not explain why the practical nurse/nursing assistant is doing the exercise.
3. Passive exercises will not increase muscle strength.
4. Isotonic exercises are useful for strengthening the muscle, but it is necessary to contract the muscle. Therefore, it would not be passive exercise.

CLASSIFICATION

Competency Category:	Client Care – Implementation
Taxonomic Level:	Critical Thinking
Client Age:	Child & Adolescent

REFERENCES

Hood & Dincher (1992), p. 265
Kozier et al. (1991), p. 866

57 CORRECT ANSWER: 3

1. Tying the client's hair may decrease the tendency to tangle, but the practical nurse/nursing assistant is imposing a decision on the client without allowing her input.
2. A secured braid will prevent tangles but does not address the client's right to have input into her care decisions.
3. Styling the client's hair based on her input recognizes her right to participate in care decisions.
4. Suggesting that the client's hair be cut places her in an uncomfortable decision-making position that does not address the tangling problem realistically.

CLASSIFICATION

Competency Category:	Client Care – Implementation
Taxonomic Level:	Application
Client Age:	Older Adult

REFERENCES

Kozier et al. (1993), p. 426
Perry & Potter (1994), p. 150

58 CORRECT ANSWER: 2

1. The practical nurse/nursing assistant would not have access to the oral cavity when the client is in the prone position.
2. The side-lying position prevents aspiration by allowing secretions to drain from the client's mouth instead of collecting in the back of the throat.
3. The client could aspirate in the semi-Fowler's position as secretions collect in the back of the throat.
4. The risk of aspiration rather than comfort is the primary focus when performing mouth care for an unconscious client.

CLASSIFICATION

Competency Category:	Client Care – Implementation
Taxonomic Level:	Application
Client Age:	Child & Adolescent

REFERENCES

Potter & Perry (1991), p. 699
Sorrentino (1992), p. 198

59 CORRECT ANSWER: 4

1. Placement of the body on a shroud would be done after the family had visited.
2. Removal of jewelry could be done before the family leaves so that they can take the valuables home with them.
3. Collection of the client's personal effects would take place after family viewing.
4. Preparation of the body for family viewing should be the first intervention because the family usually wishes to see the loved one.

CLASSIFICATION

Competency Category:	Client Care – Implementation
Taxonomic Level:	Application
Client Age:	General

REFERENCES

Christensen & Kockrow (1994), p. 1584
Sorrentino (1992), p. 470

60 CORRECT ANSWER: 1

1. With minimal help, the client can feed himself independently.
2. The client will need assistance to prepare the tray.
3. Having the client eat his foods in a particular order will not promote his independence.
4. The client does not need to be fed.

CLASSIFICATION

Competency Category:	Client Care – Implementation
Taxonomic Level:	Application
Client Age:	Child & Adolescent

REFERENCES

deWit (1994), p. 602
Rosdahl (1991), pp. 241–242

61 CORRECT ANSWER: 2

1. Dairy products do not promote regular elimination.
2. Healthy elimination is facilitated by a daily intake of fluids (6–8 glasses/day).
3. Telling the client to go to the washroom every 4 hours is not a relevant suggestion in maintaining regular bowel elimination.
4. It is not the role of the practical nurse/nursing assistant to instruct the client to use laxatives.

CLASSIFICATION

Competency Category:	Client Care – Implementation
Taxonomic Level:	Application
Client Age:	Child & Adolescent

REFERENCES

Potter & Perry (1993), pp. 1095, 1104
Rosdahl (1991), p. 225

62 CORRECT ANSWER: 1

1. To meet the changing needs of the client, discharge planning begins at the time of admission.
2. It would be impossible to meet the changing needs of the client on the day of discharge.
3. Discharge planning is an interdisciplinary responsibility and may be initiated before any discussion with the family.
4. A physician's order is not required for discharge planning.

CLASSIFICATION

Competency Category:	Client Care – Planning
Taxonomic Level:	Knowledge/Comprehension
Client Age:	General

REFERENCES

Bolander (1994), p. 395
McCarthy et al. (1994), p. 194

63 CORRECT ANSWER: 1

1. Correct food choices are an effective way to control odor from a colostomy.
2. A frequent change of appliance is not a reasonable way to correct odor problems.
3. Using a deodorizer on a regular basis is not the most appropriate way to control odor and could cause stoma irritation.
4. Providing new equipment would not be the role of the practical nurse/nursing assistant and may not solve an odor problem.

CLASSIFICATION

Competency Category:	Client Care – Implementation
Taxonomic Level:	Knowledge/Comprehension
Client Age:	Child & Adolescent

REFERENCES

Potter & Perry (1993), pp. 1419, 1422
Suddarth (1991), p. 484

64 CORRECT ANSWER: 2

1. This action would keep the dentures moist and would make inserting the dentures easier. No teaching is required.
2. This action would cause the dentures to warp. Teaching is required.
3. This action prevents food and bacteria from collecting on the surface of the dentures. No teaching is required.
4. This action reduces the chance of breakage. No teaching is required.

CLASSIFICATION

Competency Category:	Client Care – Implementation
Taxonomic Level:	Application
Client Age:	Older Adult

REFERENCES

Potter & Perry (1991), pp. 701–702
Sorrentino (1992), p. 200

65 CORRECT ANSWER: 2

1. Patting the wound dry with a clean bath towel is not considered surgical asepsis.
2. A clean wound is cleansed from the incision outward using the principle of working from the least contaminated to the most contaminated areas. This technique prevents contamination of a clean wound.
3. While washing the hands after a dressing change is a sound practice, it is considered medical asepsis.
4. While avoiding picking at and touching the dressing is taught to prevent possible contamination of the wound, it is not considered a surgical aseptic practice.

CLASSIFICATION

Competency Category:	Client Care – Implementation
Taxonomic Level:	Application
Client Age:	Adult

REFERENCES

Kozier et al. (1991), p. 1323
Suddarth (1991), p. 73

CORRECT ANSWER: 4

1. Indicating how the client can assist is important, but his weight and condition have not been included as critical aspects of safe transfer. Assistance should be obtained for a first-time transfer.
2. It would be unsafe to involve an untrained person in a transfer procedure.
3. A mechanical lifting device might be used, but it would require two people for safe operation.
4. Requesting assistance from a nurse co-worker is the only safe route, given the client's weight and condition and the fact that this is a first-time transfer.

CLASSIFICATION

Competency Category: Professional and Personal
                        Responsibilities
Taxonomic Level: Application
Client Age: Adult

REFERENCES

Caldwell & Hegner (1989), p. 187
Potter & Perry (1993), p. 1488

 CORRECT ANSWER: 4

1. Placing the client's call bell within reach is a correct action but it does not assist the client to regain bladder control.
2. Caffeine drinks stimulate diuresis and may cause incontinence.
3. Identifying a target date will not ensure the reestablishment of bladder control.
4. Monitoring elimination patterns will allow the practical nurse/nursing assistant to develop a voiding schedule.

CLASSIFICATION

Competency Category: Client Care – Implementation
Taxonomic Level: Application
Client Age: Adult

REFERENCES

Potter & Perry (1993), pp. 1362–1363
Timby & Lewis (1992), pp. 508–509

68 CORRECT ANSWER: 1

1. Applying pressure directly over the wound helps to stop bleeding.
2. Placing a cold pack over the wound is not the recommended method to prevent bleeding.
3. Applying pressure to the brachial site will reduce blood flow to the entire arm.
4. Elevating the arm is not the initial action that should be taken.

CLASSIFICATION

Competency Category: Client Care – Implementation
Taxonomic Level: Knowledge/Comprehension
Client Age: Adult

REFERENCES

Kozier et al. (1991), p. 1308
Potter & Perry (1993), p. 1665

69 CORRECT ANSWER: 1

1. Elastic compression of the legs reduces venous blood pooling and enhances venous blood return to the heart.
2. Antiembolic stockings promote, rather than impede, venous blood return.
3. Antiembolic stockings do not affect the performance of range-of-motion exercises.
4. Antiembolic stockings do not prevent muscle contractions.

CLASSIFICATION

Competency Category: Client Care – Implementation
Taxonomic Level: Application
Client Age: General

REFERENCES

Smeltzer & Bare (1992), p. 772
Sorrentino (1992), p. 376

70 CORRECT ANSWER: 2

1. While a footboard might be used with this client, its purpose is to prevent footdrop/plantar flexion.
2. A trochanter roll is suitable because its purpose is to prevent external rotation of the hip.
3. An alternating pressure mattress relieves pressure but does not prevent hip dislocation.
4. A sheepskin is a comfort measure but does not prevent hip dislocation.

CLASSIFICATION

Competency Category: Client Care – Implementation
Taxonomic Level: Knowledge/Comprehension
Client Age: Adult

REFERENCES

Smeltzer & Bare (1992), pp. 224, 1671
Swearingen (1991), p. 58

71 CORRECT ANSWER: 2

1. Clients are taught not to support their body weight on the axillae, as pressure increases the risk to underlying nerves, which could result in partial paralysis of the arm.
2. The affected leg is always supported by crutches. Balance and base of support are maintained.
3. Making adjustments to the crutches first requires a second person to take measurements of the client. Usually the initial measurement is sufficient.
4. The practical nurse/nursing assistant is not able to provide the client with support if he should lose his balance. The practical nurse/nursing assistant should walk slightly behind and on the affected side of the client.

CLASSIFICATION

Competency Category: Client Care – Implementation
Taxonomic Level: Knowledge/Comprehension
Client Age: Child & Adolescent

REFERENCES

Kozier et al. (1993), pp. 532–533
Perry & Potter (1994), p. 909

72 CORRECT ANSWER: 2

1. It is not possible or desirable to remove all stress. The key is to develop healthy ways to deal with stress.
2. Regular attendance at teaching sessions demonstrates that the client is taking an active role in a health promotion strategy.
3. If the client was assuming responsibility for his health, he would give his own insulin injections.
4. Inspecting the feet should be done on a daily basis.

CLASSIFICATION

Competency Category:	Communication Skills
Taxonomic Level:	Critical Thinking
Client Age:	Adult

REFERENCES

Beare & Myers (1990), p. 1510
Smeltzer & Bare (1992), p. 65

73 CORRECT ANSWER: 1

1. These observations suggest impaired blood flow and require immediate attention.
2. This observation is normal; immediate reporting is not necessary.
3. This observation is normal; immediate reporting is not necessary.
4. Itching requires a comfort measure but does not require immediate reporting.

CLASSIFICATION

Competency Category:	Client Care – Assessment
Taxonomic Level:	Application
Client Age:	Child & Adolescent

REFERENCES

Bolander (1994), p. 869
Suddarth (1991), p. 781

74 CORRECT ANSWER: 4

1. This approach by the practical nurse/nursing assistant is giving the client false reassurance.
2. The client would most likely benefit from intervention at this time.
3. Reporting to the nurse-in-charge is not providing emotional support to the distressed client.
4. The statement indicates support and availability.

CLASSIFICATION

Competency Category:	Communication Skills
Taxonomic Level:	Affective
Client Age:	Child & Adolescent

REFERENCES

Smith (1992), pp. 267-282
Walston & Walston (1995), pp. 133–136

75 CORRECT ANSWER: 2

1. A 24-hour supply prepared and stored correctly is safe to use, so there is no need to waste time and frustrate the baby by preparing individual feedings.
2. Burping helps to get rid of excess swallowed air, and should be done several times during the feeding.
3. Formula should flow in drops to avoid choking.
4. Propping of bottles can lead to aspiration, choking, or blocking of the airway.

CLASSIFICATION

Competency Category: Client Care – Implementation
Taxonomic Level: Knowledge/Comprehension
Client Age: General

REFERENCES

Bobak & Jensen (1991), p. 540
London et al. (1992), p. 933

76 CORRECT ANSWER: 2

1. There is no indication the client with PVD will necessarily be dizzy. In addition, the footwear would not ensure she would not get dizzy and, therefore, not prevent injury.
2. Due to the decreased circulation from PVD, healing of tissue is delayed. Appropriate footwear should be worn at all times when the client is ambulatory.
3. This is not the primary reason for wearing footwear. The practical nurse/nursing assistant is incorrectly prioritizing comfort over safety.
4. The reason for wearing the footwear is to protect the feet, not to support them.

CLASSIFICATION

Competency Category: Client Care – Assessment
Taxonomic Level: Application
Client Age: General

REFERENCES

Black & Matassarin-Jacobs (1993), p. 1288
Suddarth (1991), p. 394

77 CORRECT ANSWER: 2

1. Because tissue turgor normally decreases in people over age 55, this is not a reliable measure.
2. The daily comparison of intake and output is an accurate means of measuring fluid intake.
3. Weight comparisons should be performed daily to provide an accurate assessment.
4. Intake of fluid that is less than output is a clinical sign of fluid volume excess.

CLASSIFICATION

Competency Category: Client Care – Implementation
Taxonomic Level: Application
Client Age: Older Adult

REFERENCES

Potter & Perry (1993), p. 1295
Taylor et al. (1993), pp. 1021–1027

78 CORRECT ANSWER: 4

1. The blood pressure cuff must be deflated slowly to ensure the accurate measurement of blood pressure.
2. The blood pressure cuff should be inflated only 30 mmHg above the expected systolic reading to avoid discomfort to the client.
3. The arm on which the blood pressure is to be assessed should be leveled with the heart for the most accurate assessment.
4. To access the brachial artery, the cuff must be at least 2.5 cm above the elbow. In addition, the cuff must be snug to ensure equal pressure on the brachial artery.

CLASSIFICATION

Competency Category: Client Care – Assessment
Taxonomic Level: Knowledge/Comprehension
Client Age: General

REFERENCES

Potter & Perry (1993), pp. 236–244
Sorrentino (1992), pp. 300–303

79 CORRECT ANSWER: 4

1. This statement is incorrect because the insertion of contact lenses is part of the role for the practical nurse/nursing assistant.
2. No special order is required to insert contact lenses.
3. The insertion of contact lenses can be done by both registered nurses and practical nurses/nursing assistants.
4. The insertion of contact lenses is within the role of the practical nurse/nursing assistant.

CLASSIFICATION

Competency Category: Professional and Personal Responsibilities
Taxonomic Level: Affective
Client Age: General

REFERENCES

Potter & Perry (1993), p. 1063
Timby & Lewis (1992), p. 107

80 CORRECT ANSWER: 2

1. Sucking on the nipple causes soreness and does not ensure the infant's gums compress the milk ducts beneath the areola to facilitate milk expression. The infant's mouth should cover the nipple and the areola.
2. Using a finger to break suction lessens the incidence of nipple soreness and breast discomfort from pulling or tension on the nipple.
3. Having the infant nurse on the same breast with each feeding can lead to nipple cracking, soreness, breast engorgement, and mastitis. Breasts should be alternated so that the infant nurses on the opposite breast initially.
4. Stimulating both of the infant's cheeks confuses a hungry infant as to where to find the food source. Only the cheek nearest the breast should be stroked to elicit the rooting reflex.

CLASSIFICATION

Competency Category: Client Care – Implementation
Taxonomic Level: Knowledge/Comprehension
Client Age: General

REFERENCES
Bobak & Jensen (1991), p. 531
London et al. (1992), pp. 925, 929

81 CORRECT ANSWER: 1

, a grasping, rolling and pressing mout to massage muscles

1. Kneading increases circulation to muscles and relieves muscle tension.
2. Long strokes are more soothing movements than short strokes.
3. Lotion to the back should be warmed because cold causes tension in the muscles.
4. Vigorous massage of sensitive areas may lead to further tissue injury.

CLASSIFICATION

Competency Category: Client Care – Implementation
Taxonomic Level: Knowledge/Comprehension
Client Age: General

REFERENCES
Potter & Perry (1993), p. 1039
Timby & Lewis (1992), pp. 98–99

82 CORRECT ANSWER: 3

1. Assumptions of cause and effect (i.e., bruised elbow) should not be reported in the documentation. If reporting on the side rail, observations of position should be documented, not conclusions.
2. This entry is an assumption of cause and effect as it assumes the client fell out of bed.
3. The details of the incident that are included are entered objectively.
4. This entry assumes the client fell out of bed and the notification of the physician has not been included.

CLASSIFICATION

Competency Category: Client Care – Assessment
Taxonomic Level: Critical Thinking
Client Age: General

REFERENCES
Potter & Perry (1993), p. 299
Sorrentino (1992), p. 123

83 CORRECT ANSWER: 3

1. Due to the client's condition, she may be unable to understand and to follow directions.
2. During a fire, hallways are to remain free of obstruction.
3. Bringing the client to the nearest room is the quickest method to ensure the safety of the client.
4. This action does indicate a fire safety practice, but the client's room may not be conveniently located.

CLASSIFICATION

Competency Category: Professional and Personal Responsibilities
Taxonomic Level: Application
Client Age: Older Adult

REFERENCES

Potter & Perry (1993), p. 1453
Rosdahl (1991), p. 300

84 CORRECT ANSWER: 4

1. Although the drainage port should not touch the measurement container, this is not a principle of universal precautions.
2. A large sterile syringe is the incorrect equipment for this procedure and does not reflect universal precautions.
3. Cleaning the port does not ensure that universal precautions are maintained.
4. Clean gloves should be worn whenever there is a risk of contact with blood or any body fluids.

CLASSIFICATION

Competency Category: Client Care – Implementation
Taxonomic Level: Application
Client Age: Adult

REFERENCES

Durham & Cohen (1991), p. 260
Potter & Perry (1993), pp. 422–426

85 CORRECT ANSWER: 4

1. Changing the appliance close to mealtime may affect the client's appetite.
2. Peeling the drainage bag off quickly will increase the client's discomfort and may cause skin breakdown.
3. Rubbing causes skin breakdown.
4. Placing the client in a standing or lying position permits easier application and decreases the chance for spilling contents during removal.

CLASSIFICATION

Competency Category: Client Care – Implementation
Taxonomic Level: Knowledge/Comprehension
Client Age: General

REFERENCES

Kozier et al. (1991), pp. 1177–1178
Rosdahl (1991), p. 857

86 CORRECT ANSWER: 3

1. This pulse is in the normal range for an adolescent. Initially, the pulse rate slows down with deterioration.
2. The severity of a headache increases with deterioration of a head injury.
3. Muscle weakness increases as neurological status deteriorates.
4. Reactive pupils are a sign that his condition is improving, not deteriorating.

CLASSIFICATION

Competency Category:	Client Care – Assessment
Taxonomic Level:	Knowledge/Comprehension
Client Age:	Child & Adolescent

REFERENCES

deWit & Keane (1992), p. 332
Potter & Perry (1993), p. 597

87 CORRECT ANSWER: 1

1. Because charts are legal documents, entries are written clearly and concisely so that they are easily understood.
2. Charts are legal documents. All entries are required to remain, whether correct or incorrect.
3. Each entry should be signed when it is written.
4. Charts are legal documents. Entries in pencil could allow for tampering.

CLASSIFICATION

Competency Category:	Communication Skills
Taxonomic Level:	Knowledge/Comprehension
Client Age:	General

REFERENCES

Bolander (1994), pp. 484–485
McCarthy et al. (1994), p. 22

88 CORRECT ANSWER: 3

1. Microorganisms will be drawn into the eyes if they are cleansed in this manner.
2. Perineal care should be given last to reduce the transmission of microorganisms to other areas of the body.
3. Long and firm, but gentle strokes help to stimulate circulation.
4. The feet and toes should not be lathered because this may aggravate the already dry skin of the elderly client.

CLASSIFICATION

Competency Category:	Client Care – Implementation
Taxonomic Level:	Application
Client Age:	Older Adult

REFERENCES

Kozier et al. (1991), p. 515
Potter & Perry (1993), pp. 1027–1035

89 CORRECT ANSWER: 2

1. The information the client is able to give may not be accurate. This is not the correct source for information.
2. The nurse-in-charge should be able to clarify the procedure and give the practical nurse/nursing assistant direction in carrying it out correctly.
3. A procedure should not be performed without complete knowledge.
4. The practical nurse/nursing assistant is neglecting personal responsibility.

CLASSIFICATION

Competency Category: Professional and Personal
                          Responsibilities
Taxonomic Level: Application
Client Age: General

REFERENCES

Sorrentino (1992), p. 20
Springhouse Corporation (1992), pp. 214–216

90 CORRECT ANSWER: 2

1. Wrapping the cord is not within the role of the practical nurse/nursing assistant.
2. Removal of the lamp eliminates the hazard, and a check by the maintenance staff allows qualified repairs to be made.
3. Using the lamp, but not touching the cord, might appear to be safe, but electrical shock is still a possibility.
4. Documentation does not ensure that the correct department gets the information to rectify the problem.

CLASSIFICATION

Competency Category: Client Care – Assessment
Taxonomic Level: Application
Client Age: General

REFERENCES

Caldwell & Hegner (1989), p. 166
Potter & Perry (1993), p. 1455

91 CORRECT ANSWER: 1

1. Stopping the oral care will allow clots to form and prevent further bleeding. The ice chips will lead to vasoconstriction.
2. It is unsafe practice for the practical nurse's/nursing assistant's ungloved hand to be in a client's bleeding mouth. Also, this action would not help stop the bleeding.
3. All oral care should be discontinued during episodes of active bleeding. In addition, hydrogen peroxide would cause further complications.
4. Pressure at the site might help, but placing the client in the low-Fowler's position could lead to blood running down the back of the throat, which could cause choking.

CLASSIFICATION

Competency Category: Client Care – Implementation
Taxonomic Level: Critical Thinking
Client Age: Older Adult

REFERENCES

Smeltzer & Bare (1992), pp. 1901–1919
Suddarth (1991), pp. 256–258

92 CORRECT ANSWER: 3

1. This statement does not provide the client with the opportunity to express her concerns and feelings.
2. The practical nurse/nursing assistant is focusing on leaving as soon as care is completed and is not giving the client the opportunity to express her concerns.
3. This response states the practical nurse's/nursing assistant's observations and opens an opportunity for the client to express her concerns.
4. The practical nurse/nursing assistant is giving advice that is not necessarily true, and the response does not allow the client to express her concerns.

CLASSIFICATION

Competency Category: Communication Skills
Taxonomic Level: Affective
Client Age: Older Adult

REFERENCES
Eliopoulos (1993), pp. 106–110
Smith (1992), pp. 93–115

93 CORRECT ANSWER: 4

1. Rechecking the elevated temperature in 30 minutes does not address the problem. This finding should be reported to the nurse-in-charge for further assessment and/or intervention.
2. This action requires a physician's order. In addition, this would not be the initial action.
3. Although this action may be appropriate, the first action the practical nurse/nursing assistant should take is to notify the nurse-in-charge.
4. The elevated temperature requires the practical nurse/nursing assistant to first report the finding to the nurse-in-charge for possible treatment and/or intervention.

CLASSIFICATION

Competency Category: Client Care – Assessment
Taxonomic Level: Application
Client Age: Child & Adolescent

REFERENCES
Potter & Perry (1991), pp. 214–219
Suddarth (1991), pp. 1142–1144

94 CORRECT ANSWER: 2

1. The supine position causes hyperextension of the hips and should be used only when a client's activity is restricted.
2. Fowler's is the most normal position for elimination and it prevents back strain.
3. Sims' position is inappropriate for using the bedpan because the client's buttocks are not in direct contact with the bedpan.
4. The dorsal recumbent position is not the most appropriate. It is usually used for clients with restricted movements of the back.

CLASSIFICATION

Competency Category:	Client Care – Implementation
Taxonomic Level:	Knowledge/Comprehension
Client Age:	General

REFERENCES

Kozier et al. (1993), p. 664
Potter & Perry (1993), p. 1408

95 CORRECT ANSWER: 3

1. Leg cramps are not an indication of a serious problem related to blood transfusion.
2. Cool extremities are not an indication of a serious problem related to blood transfusion.
3. Urticaria is an allergic reaction often associated with incompatible blood.
4. Polyuria is not an indication of a serious problem related to blood transfusion.

CLASSIFICATION

Competency Category:	Client Care – Assessment
Taxonomic Level:	Knowledge/Comprehension
Client Age:	Older Adult

REFERENCES

Hood & Dincher (1992), p. 414
Smeltzer & Bare (1992), p. 815

96 CORRECT ANSWER: 2

1. The exercises may not necessarily make the client more energetic or improve appetite. In addition, the purpose for postoperative exercise is not to improve energy or appetite.
2. The purpose of performing postoperative leg exercises is to promote blood flow in the legs and reduce the risk of the formation of blood clots.
3. Although recovery may be facilitated by doing leg exercises, it cannot be presumed that it will occur quickly.
4. Exercise does strengthen the heart but, for postoperative clients, the focus is to facilitate circulation.

CLASSIFICATION

Competency Category:	Client Care – Implementation
Taxonomic Level:	Knowledge/Comprehension
Client Age:	Child & Adolescent

REFERENCES

Black & Matassarin-Jacobs (1993), p. 411
Smeltzer & Bare (1992), p. 410

97 CORRECT ANSWER: 4

1. "Small" is not an accurate measurement and the statement lacks sufficient detail.
2. "Moderate" is not an accurate measurement, and the statement does not identify which toe or foot.
3. This statement does not identify which toe or foot the discharge is coming from.
4. Documentation should describe the type and amount of drainage, the location, and the appearance.

CLASSIFICATION

Competency Category:	Client Care – Assessment
Taxonomic Level:	Application
Client Age:	Child & Adolescent

REFERENCES

Kozier et al. (1993), p. 931
Potter & Perry (1993), p. 1662

98 CORRECT ANSWER: 3

1. These are manifestations of hyperglycemia, not of hypoglycemia.
2. These are manifestations of hyperglycemia, not of hypoglycemia.
3. These manifestations are the typical reactions the body has to low blood sugar or insulin shock.
4. These are manifestations of hyperglycemia, not of hypoglycemia.

CLASSIFICATION

Competency Category:	Client Care – Assessment
Taxonomic Level:	Knowledge/Comprehension
Client Age:	Child & Adolescent

REFERENCES

Black & Matassarin-Jacobs (1993), p. 1800
Sorrentino (1992), p. 409

99 CORRECT ANSWER: 2

1. The yellowish white scab is part of the granulating process of healing tissue.
2. The presence of redness beyond wound edges is one indication of infection.
3. This temperature is within the normal range for a newborn.
4. The smell of ammonia results from the decomposition of urine.

CLASSIFICATION

Competency Category:	Client Care – Assessment
Taxonomic Level:	Knowledge/Comprehension
Client Age:	Child & Adolescent

REFERENCES

Potter & Perry (1993), p. 1658
Whaley & Wong (1993), p. 1024

100 CORRECT ANSWER: 3

1. Ankle exercises are inappropriate until further assessment has been completed.
2. Elevating an extremity reduces edema resulting from venous congestion. In addition, elevating a limb with arterial insufficiency causes a limb to become paler.
3. Circulation to the foot is determined by assessing the pedal pulse.
4. The goal should be to determine if circulation is impaired. Although covering the client might promote overall vasodilation, it does not address the poor circulation in her foot.

CLASSIFICATION

Competency Category:	Client Care – Assessment
Taxonomic Level:	Critical Thinking
Client Age:	Adult

REFERENCES

Kozier et al. (1991), p. 336
Potter & Perry (1993), p. 478

101 CORRECT ANSWER: 3

1. This is an appropriate intervention, but it is not the initial one in this situation.
2. This is an appropriate intervention, but it is not the initial one in this situation.
3. This intervention is performed first because without this intervention, all other steps may be interrupted due to elimination needs.
4. This is an appropriate intervention, but it is not the initial one in this situation.

CLASSIFICATION

Competency Category:	Client Care – Implementation
Taxonomic Level:	Knowledge/Comprehension
Client Age:	General

REFERENCES

Kozier et al. (1991), p. 1015
Rosdahl (1991), p. 241

102 CORRECT ANSWER: 3

1. The side-lying position would not decrease pain for this client.
2. Client demonstration of ankle exercises is not the priority and can be done later.
3. Deep breathing will reexpand the lungs and eliminate anesthetic after surgery.
4. The high-Fowler's position would enhance pain for this client.

CLASSIFICATION

Competency Category:	Client Care – Implementation
Taxonomic Level:	Application
Client Age:	Older Adult

REFERENCES

Kozier et al. (1993), p. 986
Potter & Perry (1993), p. 1643

103 CORRECT ANSWER: 3

1. While discussing the benefits of a tub bath may be done, it is not the priority.
2. Explaining the procedure would not be a priority.
3. **The client has a right to determine if and how the tub bath will proceed.**
4. By telling the client when the practical nurse/nursing assistant is available, the client's right to have input in own care is being ignored.

CLASSIFICATION

Competency Category:	Professional and Personal Responsibilities
Taxonomic Level:	Affective
Client Age:	Older Adult

REFERENCES

Potter & Perry (1993), pp. 295–296
Timby & Lewis (1992), pp. 75–76

1 CORRECT ANSWER: 1

1. Acetylsalicylic acid may interact with oral anticoagulants, causing bleeding complications.
2. Acetylsalicylic acid is not contraindicated with digoxin.
3. Acetylsalicylic acid is not contraindicated with furosemide.
4. Acetylsalicylic acid is not contraindicated with lorazepam.

CLASSIFICATION

Competency Category: Client Care – Implementation
Taxonomic Level: Application
Client Age: General

REFERENCES
Baer & Williams (1992), pp. 631–633
Canadian Pharmaceutical Association (1994), p. 300

2 CORRECT ANSWER: 3

1. The practical nurse/nursing assistant would be unable to ascertain how much suppository has been absorbed. The attempt to retrieve the suppository may only push it further up into the rectum.
2. The client should be assessed prior to filling out an incident report and notifying the physician.
3. It is important to report the medication error so that the physician can prescribe treatment if necessary. The client must be assessed for possible side effects of the error.
4. The client should be assessed first. In addition, voiding would not likely decrease the absorption of the miconazole nitrate.

CLASSIFICATION

Competency Category: Client Care – Implementation
Taxonomic Level: Application
Client Age: General

REFERENCES
Potter & Perry (1993), p. 639
Spencer et al. (1993), p. 174

3 CORRECT ANSWER: 4

1. This response does not adequately answer the client's question.
2. This response is not appropriate because massaging the site may contribute to unpredictable absorption of the insulin, and may cause irritation of the site.
3. This response is not appropriate because the technique of insulin injection does not depend on the health care worker. All health care workers would be taught the same technique of medication administration.
4. Massaging after an insulin injection may contribute to unpredictable absorption of the medication and may cause irritation of the site.

CLASSIFICATION

Competency Category:	Client Care – Implementation
Taxonomic Level:	Application
Client Age:	Adult

REFERENCES

Guthrie & Guthrie (1991), p. 115
Taylor et al. (1993), p. 1224

4 CORRECT ANSWER: 2

1. This response is not appropriate because it should not be assumed that the client is addicted to the medication.
2. This response addresses the family's concerns and demonstrates knowledge of the medication and the implications for the total care plan.
3. This response is not appropriate because the family's concerns about addiction are not addressed.
4. This response is not appropriate because the discussion of a client's care plan and goals are within the role and professional responsibility of the practical nurse/nursing assistant.

CLASSIFICATION

Competency Category:	Client Care – Implementation
Taxonomic Level:	Critical Thinking
Client Age:	General

REFERENCES

Johnson et al. (1992), pp. 562–564
Shlafer & Marieb (1989), pp. 353–354

5 CORRECT ANSWER: 2

1. Crushed pills can be mixed in any amount of liquid.
2. A crushed pill disintegrates immediately, and absorption from the gastrointestinal tract occurs rapidly.
3. The client's weight is not the most important factor to consider before administration of this medication.
4. Vital signs are not the most important factors to consider before administration of this medication.

CLASSIFICATION

Competency Category:	Client Care – Implementation
Taxonomic Level:	Application
Client Age:	General

REFERENCES

Baer & Williams (1992), p. 125
Deglin & Vallerand (1994), p. 82

6 CORRECT ANSWER: 2

1. Antitussive is a cough suppressant.
2. **Anesthetic provides relief of painful hemorrhoids.**
3. Antiseptic would not alleviate the manifestations of hemorrhoids.
4. Antipyretic is used to relieve fever.

CLASSIFICATION

Competency Category: Client Care – Implementation
Taxonomic Level: Knowledge/Comprehension
Client Age: General

REFERENCES

Deglin & Vallerand (1994), pp. 1173–1174
Loebl et al. (1994), pp. 844–845

7 CORRECT ANSWER: 1

1. **It is always important to document the toleration of the procedure.**
2. It is not the role of the practical nurse/nursing assistant to assess the vaginal mucosa, because it requires the insertion of a speculum.
3. There are many factors that determine position. This information is not the most important to document.
4. Medical aseptic technique must be used for all vaginal medications. In addition, it does not need to be documented on the client's chart.

CLASSIFICATION

Competency Category: Client Care – Implementation
Taxonomic Level: Application
Client Age: General

REFERENCES

Kozier et al. (1991), pp. 1300–1301
Potter & Perry (1993), pp. 683–684

8 CORRECT ANSWER: 3

1. The effects of a narcotic analgesic are blocked by antagonists.
2. Most narcotics have the ability to interact with other central nervous system depressants.
3. **Narcotics usually produce greater analgesia than that produced by higher dosages of non-narcotics.**
4. Narcotics do not cause uniform depression but, rather, react specifically with isolated membranes in the brain and spinal cord.

CLASSIFICATION

Competency Category: Client Care – Implementation
Taxonomic Level: Knowledge/Comprehension
Client Age: General

REFERENCES

Johnson et al. (1992), pp. 567–569
Shlafer & Marieb (1989), pp. 332–335

9 CORRECT ANSWER: 3

1. Having the client list all of his known allergies is not the first priority in this situation. In addition, this client may be in a life-threatening situation in a short period of time.
2. There may be differences between the two medications, however, cross-reactions are common for clients who react to one penicillin. Discussing the medications may delay obtaining treatment.
3. The client's description of his previous reaction would be helpful in planning appropriate nursing and medical treatments.
4. Monitoring blood pressure and respirations would likely be part of treatment, but initially it is necessary to ascertain the extent of his allergy.

CLASSIFICATION

Competency Category:	Client Care – Implementation
Taxonomic Level:	Critical Thinking
Client Age:	General

REFERENCES

Black & Matassarin-Jacobs (1993), pp. 456, 564-565
Shlafer & Marieb (1989), pp. 1138–1139

10 CORRECT ANSWER: 3

1. Delaying teaching until the client has accepted her need for insulin injections may indefinitely delay essential learning for her.
2. Focusing on preparation of the syringe and dietary concerns will not help the client learn to administer her own insulin.
3. Arranging practice sessions will assist in helping the client to overcome her fear of syringes and injections and will give her an opportunity to express her fears.
4. Instructing the client's mother to administer the injections is a supportive approach, but it does not help the client to administer her own insulin.

CLASSIFICATION

Competency Category:	Client Care – Implementation
Taxonomic Level:	Application
Client Age:	Child & Adolescent

REFERENCES

Guthrie & Guthrie (1991), pp. 116–119
Phipps et al. (1991), p. 1123

11 CORRECT ANSWER: 3

1. Drinking plenty of fluids is more appropriate for a hyperglycemic reaction. The client is exhibiting manifestations of a hypoglycemic reaction.
2. Overtreatment should be avoided because it may cause a sharp increase in blood glucose, and the client may experience hyperglycemia for hours after treatment. Ten mL of sugar (2 teaspoons) is adequate. The practical nurse/nursing assistant should assess blood sugar to confirm the diagnosis of hypoglycemia before notifying the nurse-in-charge.
3. **The first priority would be to administer an appropriate amount of a fast-acting sugar to the client and then measure the client's blood glucose.**
4. This intervention is not a priority because the client is still able to take glucose orally.

CLASSIFICATION

Competency Category:	Client Care – Implementation
Taxonomic Level:	Application
Client Age:	Adult

REFERENCES
Guthrie & Guthrie (1991), p. 191
Phipps et al. (1991), p. 1119

12 CORRECT ANSWER: 3

1. A paper mask would not be effective in preventing the practical nurse/nursing assistant from inhaling the medicated mist.
2. The safety concern is that the practical nurse/nursing assistant may inhale some of the medicated mist. Wearing gloves does not address this issue.
3. **By not inhaling the mist, the practical nurse/nursing assistant will avoid becoming medicated. The practical nurse/nursing assistant could be positioned to avoid any inhalation.**
4. A venturi mask would not prevent the mist from being emitted into the air. An aerochamber cannot be used to administer liquid medication.

CLASSIFICATION

Competency Category:	Client Care – Implementation
Taxonomic Level:	Application
Client Age:	General

REFERENCES
deWit (1994), pp. 869, 1063
Kozier et al. (1993), pp. 847–849

13 CORRECT ANSWER: 2

1. Application of heat generally needs to be ordered. In addition, it does not address the effects of the narcotic and the client's decreased mobility.
2. Constipation is a common side effect of immobility and narcotics. Encouraging the intake of fluids, prune juice, and bran will help reduce the risk of constipation for this client.
3. Apple juice is not appropriate because it has a constipating effect, and a wholewheat muffin has less fibre than bran. In addition, fluid intake has not been increased.
4. If a client is in pain, pain medication should not be withheld. Dependency on medication is not a concern when a client is experiencing chronic pain.

CLASSIFICATION

Competency Category:	Client Care – Implementation
Taxonomic Level:	Critical Thinking
Client Age:	Older Adult

REFERENCES

Canadian Pharmaceutical Association (1994), p. 266
Kozier et al. (1991), pp. 1159, 1166

14 CORRECT ANSWER: 2

1. It is not necessary to check blood pressure when administering this particular medication.
2. Bradycardia is a serious side effect, and this medication should be withheld if the client's rate falls below 60 beats/min.
3. It is not necessary to assess respirations when administering this particular medication.
4. Although edema should be noted and reported, it does not indicate that this medication should be withheld.

CLASSIFICATION

Competency Category:	Client Care – Implementation
Taxonomic Level:	Application
Client Age:	General

REFERENCES

Loebl et al. (1994), p. 432
Spencer et al. (1993), p. 543

15 CORRECT ANSWER: 4

1. Inserting the suppository 2 cm may not be enough to prevent it from slipping out.
2. If the suppository is warmed, it may not be possible to insert it into the vagina.
3. The suppository cannot be inserted as deeply along the anterior wall because the cervix protrudes into the superior portion of the anterior wall.
4. Inserting the suppository along the posterior wall of the vagina decreases discomfort for the client. It also ensures equal distribution of the medication and decreases the risk of the suppository slipping out.

CLASSIFICATION

Competency Category:	Client Care – Implementation
Taxonomic Level:	Knowledge/Comprehension
Client Age:	General

REFERENCES

Kozier et al. (1991), pp. 1300–1301
Potter & Perry (1993), p. 683

16 CORRECT ANSWER: 4

1. While it may take 2 weeks for an anal itch to clear up, a report of burning may indicate a sensitivity reaction.
2. A cool, soothing bath may be helpful, but if the client is having a sensitivity reaction, the best approach is to have the medication changed or discontinued.
3. If the problem is a sensitivity reaction, the best approach would be to have the medication changed or discontinued.
4. Burning may indicate a sensitivity reaction. The nurse-in-charge should be notified so that the medication order can be changed if indicated.

CLASSIFICATION

Competency Category:	Client Care – Implementation
Taxonomic Level:	Application
Client Age:	General

REFERENCES

Deglin & Vallerand (1994), pp. 1168–1171
Kozier et al. (1993), p. 823

17 CORRECT ANSWER: 2

1. The semi-Fowler's position may diminish the ability to take a deep breath. Breathing deeply is required to ensure medication distribution.
2. Coughing is often increased when the client is lying flat. Greater comfort is attained if the client is placed in the sitting position, with increased lung expansion and medication distribution.
3. The low-Fowler's position may increase the probability of coughing and thus interfere with deep breathing and medication distribution.
4. The probability of coughing is increased when the client is lying flat. The potential for deep breathing and medication distribution is diminished.

CLASSIFICATION

Competency Category:	Client Care – Implementation
Taxonomic Level:	Knowledge/Comprehension
Client Age:	General

REFERENCES

Asperheim (1992), p. 121
Malseed (1990), p. 5

18 CORRECT ANSWER: 3

1. This response focuses on the needs of the caregivers and the medical therapy. The client should be provided with an opportunity to express his reasons for noncompliance.
2. This response would not encourage the client to disclose the reasons for his noncompliance with the prescribed medication.
3. This response would provide an opportunity for the client to describe his reasons for his noncompliance with the prescribed medication.
4. This response deals only with the reason why the physician has ordered the medication. It does not provide the best opportunity for the client to discuss his feelings about the medication.

CLASSIFICATION

Competency Category:	Client Care – Assessment
Taxonomic Level:	Application
Client Age:	General

REFERENCES

Shlafer & Marieb (1989), pp. 102–104
Timby & Lewis (1992), p. 598

19 CORRECT ANSWER: 4

1. Remaining supine facilitates melting and spreading of the medication only.
2. Applying a pad is a comfort measure to prevent leakage and staining.
3. Removing gloves by turning them inside out helps to prevent cross-infection, not reinfection.
4. The applicator could become a vehicle for reinfection and should be washed after each use.

CLASSIFICATION

Competency Category:	Client Care – Implementation
Taxonomic Level:	Application
Client Age:	General

REFERENCES

deWit (1994), p. 914
Timby & Lewis (1992), p. 596

20 CORRECT ANSWER: 2

1. Ophthalmic suspensions are not administered orally.
2. Ophthalmic suspensions are administered via eye drop.
3. Nasal spray is not the correct route to administer an ophthalmic suspension.
4. Inhalation is not the correct route to administer an ophthalmic suspension.

CLASSIFICATION

Competency Category:	Client Care – Implementation
Taxonomic Level:	Knowledge/Comprehension
Client Age:	General

REFERENCES

Deglin & Vallerand (1995), pp. 847–848
Kozier et al. (1993), p. 839

21 CORRECT ANSWER: 2

1. Crushing enteric-coated pills would destroy the protective coating, which helps to prevent gastrointestinal irritation.
2. Since the client has difficulty swallowing pills, she may require administration of the medication in another form. The practical nurse/nursing assistant would be required to inform the nurse-in-charge of the situation before taking any further action.
3. Enteric-coated pills would not likely dissolve in water.
4. It is not the role of the practical nurse/nursing assistant to change the form of medication to be administered.

CLASSIFICATION

Competency Category: Client Care – Implementation
Taxonomic Level: Application
Client Age: General

REFERENCES

Kozier et al. (1993), pp. 824–825
Timby & Lewis (1992), pp. 584–585

CHAPTER 7

1 CORRECT ANSWER: 2

1. Rate is managed by the infusion control device and does not need to be checked first.
2. Solution type and amount to be absorbed are the elements not being managed by the infusion control device. Therefore, they need to be checked first.
3. Rate is managed by the infusion control device, which makes position for gravity irrelevant. Rate could be checked later to ensure setting of the device is as ordered.
4. Rate is managed by the infusion control device, which makes position for gravity irrelevant. Rate could be checked later to ensure setting of the device is as ordered.

CLASSIFICATION

Competency Category:	Client Care – Implementation
Taxonomic Level:	Critical Thinking
Client Age:	General

REFERENCES

deWit (1994), p. 969
Potter & Perry (1993), pp. 1311–1313

2 CORRECT ANSWER: 2

1. Type B blood has anti-A antibodies in the serum.
2. Type A blood has anti-B antibodies in the serum.
3. Type AB blood has no antibodies in the serum.
4. Type O blood has both anti-A and anti-B antibodies in the serum.

CLASSIFICATION

Competency Category:	Client Care – Implementation
Taxonomic Level:	Knowledge/Comprehension
Client Age:	General

REFERENCES

Black & Matassarin-Jacobs (1993), p. 1322
Canadian Red Cross Society (1993), p. 36

3 CORRECT ANSWER: 1

1. Albumin is the blood product of choice for deficiency of plasma protein.
2. Plasma is the blood product of choice for multiple coagulation deficiencies, when specific factors have not been isolated or are not available.
3. Whole blood and packed cells are the blood products of choice to treat low hemoglobin.
4. Platelets are the blood product of choice for treating deficiency of platelets.

CLASSIFICATION

Competency Category:	Client Care – Implementation
Taxonomic Level:	Knowledge/Comprehension
Client Age:	General

REFERENCES

Kuhn (1994), p. 729
Perry & Potter (1994), p. 646

4 CORRECT ANSWER: 4

1. Handwashing is an important step, but is not the first intervention that should be implemented by the practical nurse/nursing assistant.
2. This intervention complies with the request of the nurse-in-charge; however, the practical nurse/nursing assistant should check the physician's order first.
3. Although this is an important step, it is not the priority at this time.
4. The practical nurse/nursing assistant should always check the physician's order prior to preparing the solution.

CLASSIFICATION

Competency Category:	Client Care – Implementation
Taxonomic Level:	Application
Client Age:	General

REFERENCES

Kozier et al. (1991), p. 1070
Potter & Perry (1991), p. 874

5 CORRECT ANSWER: 2

1. There is no need to slow the infusion rate; the practical nurse/nursing assistant should have sufficient time to check the physician's order.
2. The first intervention of the practical nurse/nursing assistant is to determine the need for further intravenous solution. This would be accomplished by checking the physician's order.
3. The first priority for the practical nurse/nursing assistant is to check the physician's order.
4. This intervention is an appropriate step, in case the intravenous site needs to be changed. However, the physician's order must be read first to establish that the intravenous is to be continued.

CLASSIFICATION

Competency Category:	Client Care – Implementation
Taxonomic Level:	Application
Client Age:	General

REFERENCES

Kozier et al. (1993), pp. 601–602
Perry & Potter (1994), p. 625

CORRECT ANSWER: 3

1. The client information and blood product must be verified and the blood bank requisition co-signed by a registered nurse; asking another practical nurse/nursing assistant to carry out this function is wrong under any circumstances.
2. The client information and blood product must be verified and the blood bank requisition co-signed by a registered nurse; however, to wait without informing the registered nurse is not appropriate because it may delay treatment.
3. The client information and blood product must be verified and the blood bank requisition co-signed by a registered nurse. The first action of the practical nurse/nursing assistant should be to notify the registered nurse that the blood product is ready to be checked and to let the registered nurse decide how to manage the situation.
4. The client information and blood product must be verified and the blood bank requisition co-signed by a registered nurse. However, it is not the best action of the practical nurse/nursing assistant to first call the nurse-in-charge who is off the unit because it may delay treatment.

CLASSIFICATION

Competency Category:	Client Care – Implementation
Taxonomic Level:	Critical Thinking
Client Age:	General

REFERENCES
Kozier et al. (1993), p. 618
Perry & Potter (1994), p. 653

7 **CORRECT ANSWER: 2**

1. This action protects the health care workers, not the client.
2. This action is an important step in ensuring the client's safety.
3. The use of double gloves is not necessary to discontinue an I.V.; single gloves are required to maintain universal precautions for client safety.
4. This action is done to prevent the solution from leaking. Otherwise, the solution could get on the client, which would be uncomfortable but not unsafe.

CLASSIFICATION

Competency Category:	Client Care – Implementation
Taxonomic Level:	Application
Client Age:	General

REFERENCES
Kozier et al. (1993), p. 605
Perry & Potter (1994), p. 631

8 CORRECT ANSWER: 3

1. The I.V. is running too slowly.
2. The drop rate of the I.V. must be increased.
3.

$$\text{Drop rate} = \frac{\text{hourly infusion rate x tubing drip factor}}{60 \text{ min/h}}$$

$$\text{Drop rate} = \frac{125 \text{ mL/h x 15 gtt/mL}}{60 \text{ min/h}} = 31.25 \text{ gtt/min}$$

The drop rate should be increased to 31 gtt/min.
4. A drop rate of 56 gtt/min is too fast.

CLASSIFICATION

Competency Category:	Client Care – Implementation
Taxonomic Level:	Application
Client Age:	General

REFERENCES

Perry & Potter (1994), p. 621
Smith & Johnson (1990), p. 169

9 CORRECT ANSWER: 1

1. Whole blood is a different blood product from packed cells. The practical nurse/nursing assistant should question the lab about the error before proceeding.
2. An error of this type should be noted and action taken immediately at the lab.
3. This would be a major error because the blood product is incorrect.
4. This would only be correct if the error was not noted in the lab, where it should have been, before returning to the nursing station.

CLASSIFICATION

Competency Category:	Client Care – Implementation
Taxonomic Level:	Application
Client Age:	General

REFERENCES

Black & Matassarin-Jacobs (1993), pp. 1387–1392
Canadian Red Cross Society (1993), pp. 11–12

10 CORRECT ANSWER: 2

1. Checking the client's identification band is correct. However, checking it with the physician's order does not actually verify the client's identity.
2. Checking the client's identification band and asking the client to state own name provides the most accurate means of identification.
3. Response to a name is not necessarily accurate. If the client is hearing impaired, the response may be inaccurate.
4. Asking the nurse-in-charge does not ensure the client's identity.

CLASSIFICATION

Competency Category:	Client Care – Implementation
Taxonomic Level:	Knowledge/Comprehension
Client Age:	General

REFERENCES

Kozier et al. (1993), p. 618
Potter & Perry (1991), p. 560

11 CORRECT ANSWER: 1

1. Keeping the affected limb at waist level will maintain the flow rate.
2. Elevating the limb would decrease the flow rate.
3. The client should not alter the height of the pole. Elevating the pole would increase the flow rate.
4. The client should not alter the height of the pole. Lowering the pole would decrease the flow rate.

CLASSIFICATION

Competency Category: Client Care – Implementation
Taxonomic Level: Application
Client Age: General

REFERENCES

Kozier et al. (1991), pp. 1076–1077
Perry & Potter (1994), p. 612

12 CORRECT ANSWER: 4

1. This infusion set would be used for an adult.
2. Macrodrip infusion sets are not calibrated to deliver 60 gtt/mL.
3. Microdrip infusion sets are not calibrated to deliver 10 gtt/mL.
4. Microdrip infusion sets are universally calibrated to deliver 60 gtt/mL. Small dosages and volumes are necessary for pediatric clients.

CLASSIFICATION

Competency Category: Client Care – Implementation
Taxonomic Level: Application
Client Age: Child & Adolescent

REFERENCES

Potter & Perry (1991), p. 874
Whaley & Wong (1991), p. 1267

13 CORRECT ANSWER: 4

1. Leakage from an infusion site often means infiltration has occurred, and it is important to check during an infusion. However, when discontinuing an infusion, leakage is usually caused by a roller clamp that has not been turned off.
2. The leakage is at the site. Therefore, checking the tubing is not appropriate when discontinuing the I.V. infusion.
3. This is an appropriate area to assess during infusion. However, during discontinuation of an infusion, fluid usually leaks because the roller clamp has not been turned off.
4. Leakage of fluid at the infusion site when discontinuing an infusion is usually caused by a roller clamp that has not been turned off. This is the first area to check.

CLASSIFICATION

Competency Category: Client Care – Implementation
Taxonomic Level: Application
Client Age: General

REFERENCES

Kozier et al. (1993), p. 606
Potter & Perry (1993), p. 1318

14 CORRECT ANSWER: 3

1. Although the condition of the tubing (e.g., kinks) is a factor to consider with any I.V. infusion, it is not the most important factor in this case.
2. The color of the infusion site is not likely to affect the flow rate.
3. Blood is a viscous solution; viscosity directly affects rate of flow. This is the most important factor to consider in this case.
4. Length of tubing does not determine rate of flow for any I.V. solution.

CLASSIFICATION

Competency Category: Client Care – Implementation
Taxonomic Level: Application
Client Age: General

REFERENCES

Bolander (1994), p. 1312
Potter & Perry (1993), p. 1320

15 CORRECT ANSWER: 4

1. The type of solution must be documented. In addition, it is not necessary to document the total I.V. intake, because intake and output are not a consideration during solution change.
2. The time of change must be documented. In addition, it is not necessary to document the total I.V. intake, because intake and output are not a consideration during solution change.
3. The volume infused must be documented. In addition, it is not necessary to document the total I.V. intake, because intake and output are not a consideration during solution change.
4. The type of solution, time and volume infused must all be documented.

CLASSIFICATION

Competency Category: Client Care – Implementation
Taxonomic Level: Application
Client Age: General

REFERENCES

Kozier et al. (1991), p. 1079
Timby & Lewis (1992), p. 666

16 CORRECT ANSWER: 1

1. It is essential to determine the present rate of flow.
2. Kinked tubing would be more likely to slow the rate of flow.
3. No indication has been given that the client has touched the I.V. clamp.
4. Providing the client with instructions is important, but it is not the first intervention that should be implemented.

CLASSIFICATION

Competency Category: Client Care – Implementation
Taxonomic Level: Application
Client Age: Older Adult

REFERENCES

Kozier et al. (1993), p. 601
Timby & Lewis (1992), pp. 664–665

17 CORRECT ANSWER: 4

1. Macrodrip tubing should be used when fast rates are necessary.
2. Infiltration is not caused by tubing size.
3. Microdrip tubing administers fluids slowly. A slow infusion rate does not provide the cardiovascular system with enough fluid in a dehydrated client.
4. Microdrip tubing is used when small or very precise volumes are to be administered.

CLASSIFICATION

Competency Category:	Client Care – Implementation
Taxonomic Level:	Knowledge/Comprehension
Client Age:	General

REFERENCES

Melonakos & Michelson (1995), p. 224
Rosdahl (1991), p. 495

18 CORRECT ANSWER: 2

1. Knowledge of the hemoglobin is not necessary to co-sign for blood administration.
2. The client's blood group and Rh factor are essential data to know when co-signing for blood administration to prevent errors in administration.
3. The client's red cell count is not necessary to co-sign for blood administration.
4. The client's red cell count is not necessary to co-sign for blood administration.

CLASSIFICATION

Competency Category:	Client Care – Implementation
Taxonomic Level:	Application
Client Age:	General

REFERENCES

Kozier et al. (1991), p. 1083
Perry & Potter (1994), p. 653

19 CORRECT ANSWER: 4

1. This action is best performed prior to the tubing change and during routine assessments.
2. This is not the first action that should be taken; the infusion must be started and the flow regulated before other routine assessments are performed.
3. This action cannot be performed until the flow has been started and regulated.
4. This is the first action the practical nurse/nursing assistant should take to ensure that the intravenous does not become occluded.

CLASSIFICATION

Competency Category:	Client Care – Implementation
Taxonomic Level:	Knowledge/Comprehension
Client Age:	General

REFERENCES

Perry & Potter (1994), pp. 627–629
Timby & Lewis (1992), pp. 666–667

20 CORRECT ANSWER: 2

1. Air in the tubing does not usually increase the rate of flow.
2. There is a danger of air embolus occurring as a result of air in the tubing.
3. Air in the tubing does not usually affect the rate of flow.
4. Air in the tubing would not cause a thrombus.

CLASSIFICATION

Competency Category:	Client Care – Implementation
Taxonomic Level:	Knowledge/Comprehension
Client Age:	General

REFERENCES

deWit (1994), p. 972
Potter & Perry (1991), p. 871

ASSUMPTIONS

In developing the competencies for practical nurses/nursing assistants beginning to practice, the following assumptions were made:

- the competencies represent the outcomes of the combined knowledge, abilities, skills, attitudes, and judgment that nurses/nursing assistants possess;

- the competencies are expected of those individuals who have successfully completed a PN/NA educational program;

- the competencies are expected of those individuals who have written and passed the national PN/NA Registration/Licensure Examination and who have just been registered/licensed to practice;

- practical nurses/nursing assistants are prepared to work in a variety of settings and contexts; these settings and contexts can influence their role and scope of practice;

- practical nurses/nursing assistants work collaboratively with other health professionals under the direction of a Registered Nurse, Registered Psychiatric Nurse (in Saskatchewan and British Columbia), or physician;

- the degree of direction or supervision required by practical nurses/nursing assistants will be determined by the client's physical, psychosocial, and spiritual needs;

- practical nurses/nursing assistants care for clients throughout the life cycle and employ a systematic approach to nursing care through the application of the nursing process; and,

- practical nurses/nursing assistants are accountable for their own actions.

COMPETENCIES FOR THE CORE COMPONENT OF THE PN/NA EXAM (BY GROUP)

GROUP A   **80 COMPETENCIES**
75–80% of the Core Component

GROUP B   **27 COMPETENCIES**
10–20% of the Core Component

GROUP C   **21 COMPETENCIES**
5–15% of the Core Component

GROUP D   **49 COMPETENCIES**
1–10% of the Core Component

GROUP A

CLIENT CARE

ASSESSMENT

The practical nurse/nursing assistant...

• assesses, reports, and records temperature (e.g., oral, rectal, axilla, groin).

• assesses, reports, and records the rhythm, rate, and characteristics of the pulse rate (e.g., radial, apical, pedal, femoral, brachial, carotid).

• assesses, reports, and records the rhythm, rate, and characteristics of respiration.

• assesses, reports, and records blood pressure.

• observes, reports, and records food intake.

• measures, reports, and records intake and output.

• assesses, reports, and records data on the client's appearance.

• assesses intravenous site of insertion and reports and records findings.

• assesses, reports, and records type and amount of wound drainage.

• assesses, reports, and records changes in client's health condition (e.g., level of consciousness, speech, hearing, vision, body alignment/posture/gait).

• assesses, reports, and records skin changes (e.g., turgor, color, integrity).

• assesses, reports, and records changes in activities and behavior patterns, pain and discomfort.

• assesses, reports, and records changes in elimination.

• assesses, reports, and records changes in circulation or oxygenation.

• assesses, reports, and records abnormal actions, situations, and symptoms.

• assesses, reports, and records responses and reactions to treatments and diagnostic tests.

• assesses, reports, and records the type of assistance needed by the client in activities of daily living.

• participates in the assessment of the client's state of awareness and emotional and psychosocial needs.

• collaborates with other members of the health care team in the assessment process.

PLANNING

The practical nurse/nursing assistant...

• organizes nursing care to make the maximum use of the time available and sets priorities that reflect individual needs.

IMPLEMENTATION

Asepsis, Wound Care, & Infection Control

The practical nurse/nursing assistant...

• implements and maintains universal precautions.

• practices medical asepsis.

• applies, changes, and maintains a simple dressing/compress using medical asepsis.

Devices & Equipment

The practical nurse/nursing assistant...

• uses accessories and equipment (e.g., cradles, sandbags, trochanter rolls, footboards, backrests, sheepskins, alternating pressure mattresses) that help to prevent deformities or to minimize the adverse effects of immobility.

• uses mechanical patient lifts.

• uses safety devices as directed, including restraints (e.g., jackets, lap-belts, extremities).

Elimination

The practical nurse/nursing assistant...

• uses nursing measures to maintain regular elimination.

• assists the client to use bedpan, urinal, commode, and toilet.

• participates in bowel and bladder training and retraining programs.

• provides catheter care (e.g., maintains drainage system, empties collection bag).

Mobility

The practical nurse/nursing assistant...

• does passive exercises and encourages the client to perform active exercises and range of motion.

• uses and demonstrates proper body mechanics.

• uses correct lifting, transfer, and transport techniques and obtains assistance when required.

• provides assistance when positioning the client in bed and chair for comfort, safety, body alignment, and promotion of respiration and circulation.

• assists the client to walk, sit, or stand.

• assists with the use of ambulation devices (e.g., crutches, canes, walkers, wheelchairs).

Nutrition

The practical nurse/nursing assistant...

• helps the client to eat, if assistance is required.

• assures appropriate fluid intake.

• assists in maintaining dietary or fluid restrictions.

• serves prescribed food supplements.

Personal Hygiene

The practical nurse/nursing assistant...

• assists the client to maintain personal hygiene.

• assists the client to bathe (e.g., tub, shower, medicated, sitz, partial or complete bed bath).

• assists with/provides hair care (e.g., shampooing, grooming).

- assists with/provides facial grooming, shaving.

- assists with/provides mouth care (e.g., routine and special, dentures).

- provides routine skin care (e.g., back care).

- assists with/provides perineal care (e.g., routine, special).

- provides special skin care.

Preoperative & Postoperative Care

The practical nurse/nursing assistant...

- provides postoperative care for the stabilized client (e.g., assists with deep breathing, leg exercises and progressive ambulation, checks dressing, monitors operative site).

Respiration & Ventilation

The practical nurse/nursing assistant...

- encourages, teaches, and reinforces teaching of deep breathing and coughing exercises.

Safety & Comfort

The practical nurse/nursing assistant...

- verifies client identification.

- ensures client accessibility to call system.

- promotes client safety and comfort.

Specimen Collection & Diagnostic Testing

The practical nurse/nursing assistant...

- collects and labels urine, emesis, stool, and sputum specimens.

Teaching & Education

The practical nurse/nursing assistant...

- provides health information, as appropriate, during routine care.

- participates in providing or reinforces instructions given to the client by other health professionals.

COMMUNICATION SKILLS

The practical nurse/nursing assistant...

- provides appropriate information to and receives information from significant others.

- communicates with the client to facilitate the client's understanding.

- encourages the client's participation in the implementation of the care plan.

- encourages the client to assume responsibility for own health.

- establishes a rapport with the client.

- uses direct, indirect, and reflective questioning methods as appropriate to the individual situation.

- provides effective interpersonal interaction through active listening, nonverbal communication and verbal communication.

- promotes the client's self-esteem.

- provides the client with the opportunity to express feelings.

- provides the client and significant others with emotional support.

- encourages and creates opportunities for the client to interact socially.

- uses touch in a therapeutic manner to communicate care and concern to the client.

- demonstrates warmth, interest, empathy, trust, and honesty in interactions with the client.

- documents and updates all client information as soon as possible without compromising client safety.

- uses approved charting forms, terms, and abbreviations.

- records in a clear, concise, and legible manner.

(3)

PROFESSIONAL & PERSONAL RESPONSIBILITIES

The practical nurse/nursing assistant...

- affirms the client's consent before initiating care.

- practices within applicable legal parameters and Code of Ethics.

- protects the rights of the client, including confidentiality, privacy, dignity, and self-determination.

- assumes accountability for own actions at all times.

- verifies orders and procedures.

- maintains good personal health and hygiene.

- performs with regard to personal health and safety.

- performs within the role and meets the expected level of competence as a practical nurse/nursing assistant.

GROUP B
CLIENT CARE

ASSESSMENT

The practical nurse/nursing assistant...

- assesses, reports, and records neurological signs (e.g., responsiveness, orientation, limb strength, pupil reaction).

- assesses, reports, and records clinical signs and symptoms of shock, hemorrhage, respiratory distress.

- assesses the mother in the postpartum period (e.g., fundus, lochia, episiotomy, breasts, and nipples), and reports and records findings.

- collects, reports, and records specified information from client upon admission.

- assesses, reports, and records diabetic reactions.

- observes, reports, and records reactions to blood and blood products transfusion therapy.

- knows where emergency equipment can be located.

- collects and validates data from available sources.

- identifies, reports, and records hazards to health and safety, including faulty equipment.

- participates in the refinement and updating of the client assessment.

IMPLEMENTATION
Asepsis, Wound Care, & Infection Control

The practical nurse/nursing assistant...

- applies, changes, and maintains a simple dressing/compress using surgical asepsis.

- applies, changes, and maintains a simple wound dressing with open or closed drain.

- applies medicated gauzes or wound care products as part of a dressing.

- carries out isolation techniques.

Death

The practical nurse/nursing assistant...

- participates in meeting the needs of the dying client and client's family.

Drainage, Irrigation, & Suctioning

The practical nurse/nursing assistant...

- cares for body drainage tubes while maintaining universal precautions.

Elimination

The practical nurse/nursing assistant...

- gives enemas.

Emergency Care

The practical nurse/nursing assistant...

- performs basic first aid measures (e.g., control of bleeding, shock, etc.).

- performs basic cardiopulmonary resuscitation and emergency measures for choking victim (e.g., BCLS-level C).

Personal Hygiene

The practical nurse/nursing assistant...

- recognizes special foot care needs.

Preoperative & Postoperative Care

The practical nurse/nursing assistant...

- prepares the client for surgery (e.g., participates in preoperative teaching, does skin preparation, prepares and assists client to dress for operating room).

Respiration & Ventilation

The practical nurse/nursing assistant...

- ensures precautions and client awareness of precautions related to the use of oxygen.

COMMUNICATION SKILLS

The practical nurse/nursing assistant...

- reports and records unusual incidents and/or accidents.

PROFESSIONAL & PERSONAL RESPONSIBILITIES

The practical nurse/nursing assistant...

- reports to the appropriate authority incidents of unsafe practice or professional misconduct of nursing or other health care providers.

- maintains a level of safety on the unit in cases of emergency.

- seeks help and guidance when unable to perform safely.

- participates in fire drills, including methods and techniques of evacuation.

GROUP C

CLIENT CARE

ASSESSMENT

The practical nurse/nursing assistant...

• assesses the client's environment.

PLANNING

The practical nurse/nursing assistant...

• establishes priorities for nursing interventions.

• participates in discharge planning.

IMPLEMENTATION
Admission, Discharge, & Transfer

The practical nurse/nursing assistant...

• participates in the admission of the client.

• orients the client to the agency/unit/room.

Devices & Equipment

The practical nurse/nursing assistant...

• makes up an occupied bed.

• operates manual and electric beds and bed attachments (e.g., I.V. poles, side rails, bed boards, overbed frames, and trapeze).

• assists with care for prostheses.

• applies bandages, triangular sling and binders, cervical collars, splints, TED stockings, tensors, braces.

Maternal & Child Care

The practical nurse/nursing assistant...

• assists with routine care of the newborn (e.g., bathing, weighing, diapering, bottle feeding).

Mobility

The practical nurse/nursing assistant...

• organizes and encourages appropriate recreational and diversional activities.

Nutrition

The practical nurse/nursing assistant...

• assists the client with food selection.

• prepares the client for meals.

Personal Hygiene

The practical nurse/nursing assistant...

• assists with/provides ear and eye care.

• assists with/provides hand care (e.g., nails).

• assists with dressing/undressing.

• administers topical medications.

Safety & Comfort

The practical nurse/nursing assistant...

• promotes relaxation and sleep (e.g., quiet, darkened room).

• uses basic measures to reduce anxiety (e.g., relaxation techniques, back rub).

Teaching & Education

The practical nurse/nursing assistant...

• suggests modifications which promote client independence.

EVALUATION

The practical nurse/nursing assistant...

• continuously evaluates the nursing process and actions with the client.

GROUP D

CLIENT CARE

ASSESSMENT

The practical nurse/nursing assistant...

• measures, reports, and records height and weight.

• assesses site of circumcision and umbilicus, and reports and records findings.

• palpates bladder, and reports and records findings.

• measures, reports, and records abdominal girth.

• tests urine for glucose and ketones, and reports and records findings.

• identifies, reports, and records spiritual and cultural needs.

• identifies, reports, and records obvious learning needs of the client.

PLANNING

The practical nurse/nursing assistant...

• involves the client and significant others in the setting of objectives and goals.

• participates in the formulation of nursing diagnoses by identifying needs that require nursing intervention.

• participates in the development of nursing care plans to meet the client's needs.

• participates in establishing nursing interventions to achieve expected outcomes.

IMPLEMENTATION
Admission, Discharge, & Transfer

The practical nurse/nursing assistant...

• cares for and secures client valuables.

• participates in the discharge/transfer of the client.

Death

The practical nurse/nursing assistant...

• cares for deceased clients and their personal possessions.

• is aware of requirements for coroner's care procedures.

Devices & Equipment

The practical nurse/nursing assistant...

• prepares a stretcher.

• prepares a crib.

• cares for client in traction.

- cares for client in a cast.

- cares for nasogastric tubes and equipment (e.g., empties drainage bottle, checks the security of tube).

Drainage, Irrigation & Suctioning

The practical nurse/nursing assistant...

- irrigates (flushes) eyes.

- performs oral suctioning.

- unclamps/clamps gastric suction tubes.

Elimination

The practical nurse/nursing assistant...

- applies condom drainage.

- maintains continuous bladder irrigation.

- clamps and releases retention catheters.

- inserts rectal tube.

- inserts rectal suppositories.

- performs manual disimpaction of feces.

- provides ostomy care to established stomas (e.g., skin care, application collection bag).

Emergency Care

The practical nurse/nursing assistant...

- operates fire extinguishers.

Maternal & Child Care

The practical nurse/nursing assistant...

- recognizes, reports, and records external signs of

the progression of labor (e.g., rupture of membranes, level of discomfort).

- assists with postpartum exercises.

- assists with breastfeeding including the expression of breast milk.

- assists with/provides breast care.

- assists with/provides general care of episiotomy.

- performs cord care.

- cares for the circumcision site.

Personal Hygiene

The practical nurse/nursing assistant...

- assists with/provides routine foot care (e.g., skin, nails, calluses, corns).

Respiration & Ventilation

The practical nurse/nursing assistant...

- assists with setting up equipment (e.g., mask, catheter, cannula, croupettes, vaporizers), and cares for client receiving oxygenation/humidification therapy.

Safety & Comfort

The practical nurse/nursing assistant...

- administers applications of heat/cold.

Specimen Collection & Diagnostic Testing

The practical nurse/nursing assistant...

- prepares, cares for, and provides information to the client undergoing diagnostic tests or procedures.

- prepares the client for and assists with physical examination.

- takes swabs (e.g., ENT, wound).

- strains urine.

- tests blood glucose using diagnostic devices (e.g., Glucometer).

EVALUATION

The practical nurse/nursing assistant...

- collects and compares objective data regarding the outcomes of nursing actions on the client and family.

- participates with the client, family, and other health professionals in the revision of the goals, priorities, and nursing actions required.

COMMUNICATION SKILLS

The practical nurse/nursing assistant...

- provides information on support services that assist clients, families, and groups in the promotion and maintenance of health.

COMPETENCIES FOR THE MEDICATIONS COMPONENT OF THE PN/NA EXAM

The practical nurse/nursing assistant...

• prepares and administers ear, eye, and nose medications.

• prepares and administers inhalation therapy.

• inserts vaginal suppositories.

• administers vaginal creams.

• administers rectal creams.

• prepares and administers oral medications.

• prepares and administers medication through feeding tubes.

• prepares and administers subcutaneous injections.

• prepares and administers narcotic medications (i.e., rectally, orally, subcutaneously, and through feeding tubes).

• observes, reports, and records client responses to medication.

• recognizes, observes, and records side effects and adverse reactions to medications.

COMPETENCIES FOR THE INTRAVENOUS/INFUSION THERAPY COMPONENT OF THE PN/NA EXAM

The practical nurse/nursing assistant...

• sets up intravenous equipment, including electronic infusion pumps.

• checks intravenous infusion for solution ordered, rate of flow, positioning for gravity, and amount remaining to be absorbed.

• adjusts intravenous flow rate.

• changes intravenous solution bottle or bag.

• discontinues intravenous therapy.

• obtains blood products from blood bank.

• assists with client identification and co-signs for blood administration.

To obtain information on writing the PN/NA Exam, contact the registering/licensing authority for your province or territory.

**Manitoba Association of
Licensed Practical Nurses**
Unit 1–615 Kernaghan Avenue
Winnipeg MB R2C 5G8
          204-222-6743
Fax: 204-224-0166

College of Nurses of Ontario
101 Davenport Road
Toronto ON M5R 3P1
Toll free: 1-800-387-5526
          416-928-0900
Fax: 416-928-6507

Council for Nursing Assistants
LeMarchant Medical Centre
195 LeMarchant Road
St. John's NF A1C 2H5
          709-579-3843
Fax: 709-579-8268

**Board of Registration of
Nursing Assistants**
Cogswell Tower
Suite 1212
2000 Barrington Street
Halifax NS B3J 3K1
          902-423-8517
Fax: 902-425-6811

**Association of New Brunswick
Registered Nursing Assistants**
384 Smythe Street
Fredericton NB E3B 3E4
          506-453-0747
Fax: 506-459-0503

**Saskatchewan Association of
Licensed Practical Nurses**
2310 Smith Street
Regina SK S4P 2P6
          306-525-1436
Fax: 306-347-7784

**Professional Council of
Licensed Practical Nurses**
10604–170th Street
Edmonton AB T5S 1P3
          403-484-8886
Fax: 403-484-9069

**British Columbia Council
of Licensed Practical Nurses**
205–4430 Halifax Street
Burnaby BC V5C 5R4
          604-660-5750
Fax: 604-660-2899

**Prince Edward Island Nursing
Assistants' Registration Board**
P.O. Box 3235
Charlottetown PE C1A 7N9
          902-892-6315
Fax: 902-566-1745

**Department of Justice
Consumer and Commercial
Affairs**
P.O. Box 2703
Whitehorse YT Y1A 2C6
          403-667-5257
Fax: 403-667-3609

**Department of Health and
Social Services,
Nursing Services, Population
Health and Board
Development Division**
Government of the Northwest
Territories, CST-7
P.O. Box 1320
Yellowknife NT X1A 2L9
          403-920-3456
          403-920-3331
Fax: 403-873-0361

The abbreviations used in the Practice Exam are defined as follows:

AIDS	acquired immune deficiency syndrome	**mL**	millilitre(s)
° C	degrees Celsius	**mmHg**	millimetres of mercury
cm	centimetre(s)	**min**	minute(s)
gtt	drops	**n.p.o.**	nothing orally
h	hour	**p.o.**	orally
HIV	human immunodeficiency virus	**p.r.n.**	as needed
h.s.	bedtime	**q. 1–2 h.**	every 1 to 2 hours
I.V.	intravenous	**q.d.**	daily
kg	kilogram(s)	**q.s.**	as much as may be needed
L	litre(s)	**Rh**	rhesus
mg	milligram(s)	**t.i.d.**	3 times daily

Bibliography

This bibliography contains the references used to produce the Practice Exam.

Asperheim, M. K. (1992). *Pharmacology: An introductory text* (7th ed.). Philadelphia: Saunders.

Baer, C. L., & Williams, B. R. (1992). *Clinical pharmacology and nursing* (2nd ed.). Springhouse, PA: Springhouse.

Beare, P. G., & Myers, J. L. (1990). *Principles and practice of adult health nursing*. Toronto: Mosby.

Beckingham, A. C., & DuGas, B. W. (1993). *Promoting healthy aging: A nursing and community perspective.* Toronto: Mosby Yearbook.

Birchenall, J. M., & Streight, M. E. (1993). *Care of the older adult* (3rd ed.). Philadelphia: Lippincott.

Black, J. M., & Matassarin-Jacobs, E. (1993). *Luckmann and Sorenson's medical-surgical nursing: A psychophysiologic approach* (4th ed.). Philadelphia: Saunders.

Bobak, I. M., & Jensen, M. D. (1991). *Essentials of maternity nursing* (3rd ed.). St. Louis: Mosby.

Bolander. V. B. (1994). *Sorensen and Luckman's basic nursing: A psychophysiologic approach* (3rd ed.). Toronto: Saunders.

Burke, M. M., & Walsh, M. B. (1992). *Gerontological nursing: Care of the frail elderly.* Toronto: Mosby Yearbook.

Caldwell, E., & Hegner, B. R. (1989). *The nursing assistant: A nursing process approach* (5th ed.). Albany, NY: Delmar.

Canadian Nurses Association (1995). *Blueprint for the Practical Nurse/Nursing Assistant Registration/Licensure Examination.* Ottawa: Author.

Canadian Pharmaceutical Association (1994). *Compendium of pharmaceuticals and specialties* (29th ed.). Ottawa: Author.

Canadian Red Cross Society (1993). *Clinical guide to transfusion* (3rd ed.). Ottawa: Author.

Christensen, B.L., & Kockrow, E. O. (1994). *Foundations of nursing* (2nd ed.). Toronto: Mosby Yearbook.

Craven, R. F., & Hirnle, C. J. (1992). *Fundamentals of nursing: Human health and function.* Philadelphia: Lippincott.

Deglin, J. H., & Vallerand, A. H. (1994). *Davis's drug guide for nurses* (4th ed.). Philadelphia: Davis Company

deWit, S. C. (1994). *Rambo's nursing skills for clinical practice* (4th ed.). Philadelphia: Saunders.

deWit, S. C., & Keane, C. B. (1992). *Keane's essentials of medical-surgical nursing* (3rd ed.). Philadelphia: Saunders.

Dudek, S. G. (1993). *Nutrition handbook for nursing practice* (2nd ed.). Philadelphia: Lippincott.

Durham, J. D., & Cohen, F. L. (1991). *The person with AIDS: Nursing perspectives* (2nd ed.). New York: Springer.

Ebersole, P., & Hess, P. (1990). *Toward healthy aging: Human needs and nursing response* (3rd ed.). Toronto: Mosby.

Eliopoulos, C. (1993). *Gerontological nursing* (3rd ed.). Philadelphia: Lippincott.

Guthrie, D. W., & Guthrie, R. A. (1991). *Nursing management of diabetes mellitus* (3rd ed.). New York: Springer.

Hamdy, R. C., Turnbull, J. M., Clark, W., & Lancaster, M. M. (1994). *Alzheimer's disease: A handbook for caregivers* (2nd ed.). St. Louis: Mosby YearBook.

Hannah, K. J., & Rankin Zerr, S. (1992). *Pharmacology and the nursing process.* Toronto: Saunders.

Hegner, B. R., & Caldwell, E. (1992). *Nursing assistant: A nursing process approach* (6th ed.). Albany, NY: Delmar.

Hill, S. S. (1993). *Success in practical nursing: Personal and vocational issues* (2nd ed.). Philadelphia: Saunders.

Hood, G. H., & Dincher, J. R. (1992). *Total patient care: Foundations and practice* (8th ed.). Toronto: Mosby Yearbook.

Ignatavicius, D. D., & Bayne, M. V. (1991). *Medical-surgical nursing: A nursing process approach.* Philadelphia: Saunders.

Jackson, D. B., & Saunders, R. B. (1993). *Child health nursing: A comprehensive approach to the care of children and their families.* Philadelphia: Lippincott.

Johnson, G. E., Hannah, K. J., & Rankin Zerr, S. (1992). *Pharmacology and the nursing process* (3rd ed.). Toronto: Saunders.

Kozier, B., Erb, G., Blais, K., Johnson, J., & Temple, J. (1993). *Techniques in clinical nursing* (4th ed.). Don Mills, ON: Addison-Wesley.

Kozier, B., Erb, G., & Olivieri, R. (1991). *Fundamentals of nursing: Concepts, process and practice* (4th ed.). Redwood City, CA: Addison-Wesley.

Kuhn, M. A. (1994). *Pharmacotherapeutics: A nursing process approach* (3rd ed.). Philadelphia: F. A. Davis.

Lewis, S. M., & Collier, I. C. (1992). *Medical-surgical nursing: Assessment and management of clinical problems* (3rd ed.). Toronto: Mosby Yearbook.

Linton, A. (1995). *Introductory nursing care of adults.* Philadelphia: Saunders.

Loebl, S., Spratto, G. R., & Woods, A. L. (1994). *The nurse's drug handbook* (7th ed.). Albany, NY: Delmar

London, M. L., Olds, S. B., & Ladewig, P. A. (1992). *Maternal-newborn nursing: A family centered approach* (4th ed.). Menlo Park, CA: Addison-Wesley.

Long, L. (1992). *Understanding / Responding: A communication manual for nurses* (2nd ed.). Boston: Jones & Bartlett.

Mahan, L. K., Arlin, M. T., & Krause, M. V. (1992). *Krause's food, nutrition, and diet therapy* (8th ed.). Philadelphia: Saunders.

Malasanos, L., Barkauskas, V., & Stoltenberg-Allen, K. (1990). *Health assessment* (4th ed.). Toronto: Mosby Yearbook.

Malseed, R. T. (1990). *Pharmacology drug therapy and nursing considerations.* Philadelphia: Lippincott.

May, K. A., & Mahlmeister, L. R. (1994). *Maternal and neonatal nursing: Family-centered care* (3rd ed.). Philadelphia: Lippincott.

McCarthy, T., Gunther, W., & Hoffman, C. L. (1994). *The nursing assistant: Acute and long-term care.* Englewood Cliffs, NJ: Prentice-Hall.

Melonakos, K., & Michelson, S. A. (1995). *Saunders pocket reference for nurses* (2nd ed.). Philadelphia: Saunders.

Morris, J. J. (1991). *Canadian nurses and the law.* Toronto: Butterworths Canada.

Perry, A. G., & Potter P. A. (1994). *Clinical nursing skills and techniques* (3rd ed.). Toronto: Mosby.

Phillips, C. R. (1991). *Family-centered maternity/newborn care: A basic text* (3rd ed.). St. Louis: Mosby Yearbook.

Phipps, W. J., Long, B. C., Woods, N. F., & Cassmeyer, V. L. (1991). *Medical-surgical nursing: Concepts and clinical practice* (4th ed.). Toronto: Mosby.

Pillitteri, A. (1992). *Maternal and child health nursing: Care of the childbearing and childrearing family.* Philadelphia: Lippincott.

Poleman, C. M., & Peckenpaugh, N. J. (1991). *Nutrition : Essentials and diet therapy* (6th ed.). Philadelphia: Saunders.

Potter, P. A., & Perry, A. G. (1991). *Basic nursing: Theory and practice* (2nd ed.). Toronto: Mosby Yearbook.

Potter, P. A., & Perry, A. G. (1993). *Fundamentals of nursing: Concepts, process and practice* (3rd ed.). Toronto: Mosby Yearbook.

Rawlins, R. P., Williams, S. R., & Beck, C.K. (1993). *Mental health-psychiatric nursing: A holistic life-cycle approach* (3rd ed.). St. Louis: Mosby.

Redman, B. K. (1993). *The process of patient education* (7th ed.). St. Louis: Mosby Yearbook.

Reeder, S. J., Martin, L. L., & Koniak, D. (1992). *Maternity nursing: Family, newborn, and women's health care* (17th ed.). Philadelphia: Lippincott.

Rosdahl, C. B. (1991). *Textbook of basic nursing* (5th ed.). Philadelphia: Lippincott.

Scherer, J. C. (1991). *Introductory medical-surgical nursing* (5th ed.). Philadelphia: Lippincott.

Shlafer, M., & Marieb, E. N. (1989). *The nurse, pharmacology, and drug therapy.* Redwood City, CA: Addison-Wesley.

Smeltzer, S. C., & Bare, B. G. (1992). *Brunner and Suddarth's textbook of medical-surgical nursing* (7th ed.). Philadelphia: Lippincott.

Smith, A. J., & Johnson, J. Y. (1990). *Nurses' guide to clinical procedures.* Philadelphia: Lippincott.

Smith, S. (1992). *Communications in nursing: Communicating assertively and responsibly in nursing* (2nd ed.). Toronto: Mosby Yearbook.

Sorrentino, S. A. (1992). *Mosby's textbook for nursing assistants* (3rd ed.). St. Louis: Mosby Yearbook.

Spencer, R. T., Nichols, L. W., Lipton, G. B., Henderson, H. S., & West, F. M. (1993). *Clinical pharmacology and nursing management* (4th ed.). Philadelphia: Lippincott.

Springhouse Corporation. (1992). *Nurse's handbook of law and ethics.* Springhouse, PA: Author.

Springhouse Corporation (1994). *Fundamental nursing skills.* Springhouse PA: Author.

Stanhope, M., & Lancaster, J. (1992). *Community health nursing: Process and practice for promoting health* (3rd ed.). Toronto: Mosby Yearbook.

Suddarth, D. S. (1991). *The Lippincott manual of nursing practice* (5th ed.). Philadelphia: Lippincott.

Swearingen, P.L. (1991). *Photo atlas of nursing procedures* (2nd ed.). Redwood City, CA: Addison-Wesley.

Taylor, C., Lillis, C., & LeMone, P. (1993). *Fundamentals of nursing: The art and science of nursing care* (2nd ed.). Philadelphia: Lippincott.

Thompson, E. D. (1990). *Introduction to maternity and pediatric nursing*. Philadelphia: Saunders.

Timby, B. K., & Lewis, L. W. (1992). *Fundamental skills and concepts in patient care* (5th ed.). Philadelphia: Lippincott.

Townsend, Mary C. (1993). *Psychiatric/mental health nursing: Concepts of care*. Philadelphia: F. A. Davis.

Walston, E. J., & Walston, K. E. (1995). *The nurse aide in long-term care*. Albany, NY: Delmar.

Whaley, L. F., & Wong, D. L. (1991). *Nursing care of infants and children* (4th ed.). Toronto: Mosby Yearbook.

Whaley, L. F., & Wong, D. L. (1993). *Whaley & Wong's essentials of pediatric nursing* (4th ed.). Toronto: Mosby Yearbook.

Wilson, H. S., & Kneisl, C. R. (1992). *Psychiatric nursing* (4th ed.). Redwood City, CA: Addison-Wesley.

Yeo, M. T. (1991). *Concepts and cases in nursing ethics*. Peterborough, ON: Broadview.

SCORING THE PN/NA PRACTICE EXAM
PERFORMANCE PROFILE TALLY SHEET

COMPETENCY CATEGORY	TOTAL INCORRECT		% INCORRECT
CLIENT CARE			
• Assessment	÷ 51 X 100 =		%
• Planning	÷ 6 X 100 =		%
• Implementation			
– *Core Component only*	÷ 102 X 100 =		%
– *Core & Medications*	÷ 123 X 100 =		%
– *Core, Medications, &* *Intravenous/Infusion Therapy*	÷ 143 X 100 =		%
• Evaluation	÷ 2 X 100 =		%
COMMUNICATION SKILLS	÷ 28 X 100 =		%
PROFESSIONAL & PERSONAL RESPONSIBILITIES	÷ 17 X 100 =		%

SCORING THE PN/NA PRACTICE EXAM
PERFORMANCE PROFILE CHART

COMPETENCY CATEGORY

% OF INCORRECT ANSWERS	0	5	10	15	20	25	30	35	40	45	50	55	60	65	70	75	80	85	90	95

CLIENT CARE

- Assessment
- Planning
- Implementation*
- Evaluation

COMMUNICATION SKILLS

PROFESSIONAL & PERSONAL RESPONSIBILITIES

* Use either the *Core Component* **only**, the *Core & Medications* Components **or** the *Core, Medications & Intravenous/Infusion Therapy* Components, as appropriate.

ANSWER SHEET
(See instructions on reverse)

FEUILLE-RÉPONSES
(Voir les instructions au verso)

Family Name - Nom de famille | First Name - Prénom

Date of Birth - Date de naissance | Date of Writing - Date de l'épreuve

/ | /

DY - JR   MO   YR - AN | DY - JR   MO   YR - AN

Test - Épreuve

| Language of Writing - Langue |
| English ○ | Français ○ |

Candidate Number
Numéro d'identité

Writing Centre Code
Code du centre

Test Form
Formulaire

#					#					#					#					#					#			
1	① ② ③ ④				31	① ② ③ ④				61	① ② ③ ④				91	① ② ③ ④				121	① ② ③ ④				151	① ② ③ ④			
2	① ② ③ ④				32	① ② ③ ④				62	① ② ③ ④				92	① ② ③ ④				122	① ② ③ ④				152	① ② ③ ④			
3	① ② ③ ④				33	① ② ③ ④				63	① ② ③ ④				93	① ② ③ ④				123	① ② ③ ④				153	① ② ③ ④			
4	① ② ③ ④				34	① ② ③ ④				64	① ② ③ ④				94	① ② ③ ④				124	① ② ③ ④				154	① ② ③ ④			
5	① ② ③ ④				35	① ② ③ ④				65	① ② ③ ④				95	① ② ③ ④				125	① ② ③ ④				155	① ② ③ ④			
6	① ② ③ ④				36	① ② ③ ④				66	① ② ③ ④				96	① ② ③ ④				126	① ② ③ ④				156	① ② ③ ④			
7	① ② ③ ④				37	① ② ③ ④				67	① ② ③ ④				97	① ② ③ ④				127	① ② ③ ④				157	① ② ③ ④			
8	① ② ③ ④				38	① ② ③ ④				68	① ② ③ ④				98	① ② ③ ④				128	① ② ③ ④				158	① ② ③ ④			
9	① ② ③ ④				39	① ② ③ ④				69	① ② ③ ④				99	① ② ③ ④				129	① ② ③ ④				159	① ② ③ ④			
10	① ② ③ ④				40	① ② ③ ④				70	① ② ③ ④				100	① ② ③ ④				130	① ② ③ ④				160	① ② ③ ④			
11	① ② ③ ④				41	① ② ③ ④				71	① ② ③ ④				101	① ② ③ ④				131	① ② ③ ④				161	① ② ③ ④			
12	① ② ③ ④				42	① ② ③ ④				72	① ② ③ ④				102	① ② ③ ④				132	① ② ③ ④				162	① ② ③ ④			
13	① ② ③ ④				43	① ② ③ ④				73	① ② ③ ④				103	① ② ③ ④				133	① ② ③ ④				163	① ② ③ ④			
14	① ② ③ ④				44	① ② ③ ④				74	① ② ③ ④				104	① ② ③ ④				134	① ② ③ ④				164	① ② ③ ④			
15	① ② ③ ④				45	① ② ③ ④				75	① ② ③ ④				105	① ② ③ ④				135	① ② ③ ④				165	① ② ③ ④			
16	① ② ③ ④				46	① ② ③ ④				76	① ② ③ ④				106	① ② ③ ④				136	① ② ③ ④				166	① ② ③ ④			
17	① ② ③ ④				47	① ② ③ ④				77	① ② ③ ④				107	① ② ③ ④				137	① ② ③ ④				167	① ② ③ ④			
18	① ② ③ ④				48	① ② ③ ④				78	① ② ③ ④				108	① ② ③ ④				138	① ② ③ ④				168	① ② ③ ④			
19	① ② ③ ④				49	① ② ③ ④				79	① ② ③ ④				109	① ② ③ ④				139	① ② ③ ④				169	① ② ③ ④			
20	① ② ③ ④				50	① ② ③ ④				80	① ② ③ ④				110	① ② ③ ④				140	① ② ③ ④				170	① ② ③ ④			
21	① ② ③ ④				51	① ② ③ ④				81	① ② ③ ④				111	① ② ③ ④				141	① ② ③ ④				171	① ② ③ ④			
22	① ② ③ ④				52	① ② ③ ④				82	① ② ③ ④				112	① ② ③ ④				142	① ② ③ ④				172	① ② ③ ④			
23	① ② ③ ④				53	① ② ③ ④				83	① ② ③ ④				113	① ② ③ ④				143	① ② ③ ④				173	① ② ③ ④			
24	① ② ③ ④				54	① ② ③ ④				84	① ② ③ ④				114	① ② ③ ④				144	① ② ③ ④				174	① ② ③ ④			
25	① ② ③ ④				55	① ② ③ ④				85	① ② ③ ④				115	① ② ③ ④				145	① ② ③ ④				175	① ② ③ ④			
26	① ② ③ ④				56	① ② ③ ④				86	① ② ③ ④				116	① ② ③ ④				146	① ② ③ ④				176	① ② ③ ④			
27	① ② ③ ④				57	① ② ③ ④				87	① ② ③ ④				117	① ② ③ ④				147	① ② ③ ④				177	① ② ③ ④			
28	① ② ③ ④				58	① ② ③ ④				88	① ② ③ ④				118	① ② ③ ④				148	① ② ③ ④				178	① ② ③ ④			
29	① ② ③ ④				59	① ② ③ ④				89	① ② ③ ④				119	① ② ③ ④				149	① ② ③ ④				179	① ② ③ ④			
30	① ② ③ ④				60	① ② ③ ④				90	① ② ③ ④				120	① ② ③ ④				150	① ② ③ ④				180	① ② ③ ④			

INSTRUCTIONS

- Use black lead pencil only (HB).

- Do NOT use ink or ballpoint pens.

- Completely fill the ovals.

- N'utilisez qu'un crayon HB.

- Ne PAS utiliser de stylo.

- Noircissez les ovales complètement.

EXAMPLES/EXEMPLES

Right/Correct

Wrong/Incorrect

- Completely erase any answer you wish to change.

- Do NOT make any stray marks on the answer sheet.

- Do not fold or staple the answer sheet.

- Effacez complètement les réponses que vous voulez changer.

- Ne faites AUCUNE autre marque sur la feuille-réponses.

- Ne pas plier ou agrafer la feuille-réponses.

COMPLETE THE IDENTIFICATION PORTION OF YOUR ANSWER SHEET

- Print your name, date of birth, date of the examination and name of the examination (from the cover of your test booklet). Fill the oval corresponding to the language of writing.

- Print, in the appropriate boxes, your candidate number, writing centre code, and test form number (from the cover of your test booklet).

- Fill in the corresponding oval for each digit.

REMPLISSEZ LA PARTIE RENSEIGNEMENTS DE VOTRE FEUILLE-RÉPONSES

- Inscrivez votre nom, votre date de naissance, la date de l'examen et le nom de l'examen (apparaissant sur la page couverture de votre cahier d'examen). Noircissez l'ovale correspondant à la langue de l'examen.

- Inscrivez, dans les espaces appropriés, le numéro d'identité, le code du centre d'examen, et le numéro du formulaire de l'épreuve (apparaissant sur la page couverture de votre cahier d'examen).

- Noircissez l'ovale correspondant à chaque lettre ou chiffre.

ANSWER SHEET
(See instructions on reverse)

FEUILLE-RÉPONSES
(Voir les instructions au verso)

Family Name - Nom de famille	First Name - Prénom

Date of Birth - Date de naissance	Date of Writing - Date de l'épreuve
/ / DY - JR MO YR - AN	/ / DY - JR MO YR - AN

Test - Épreuve

Language of Writing - Langue	
English ○	Français ○

Candidate Number / Numéro d'identité

Writing Centre Code / Code du centre

Test Form / Formulaire

1 ①②③④	31 ①②③④	61 ①②③④	91 ①②③④	121 ①②③④	151 ①②③④
2 ①②③④	32 ①②③④	62 ①②③④	92 ①②③④	122 ①②③④	152 ①②③④
3 ①②③④	33 ①②③④	63 ①②③④	93 ①②③④	123 ①②③④	153 ①②③④
4 ①②③④	34 ①②③④	64 ①②③④	94 ①②③④	124 ①②③④	154 ①②③④
5 ①②③④	35 ①②③④	65 ①②③④	95 ①②③④	125 ①②③④	155 ①②③④
6 ①②③④	36 ①②③④	66 ①②③④	96 ①②③④	126 ①②③④	156 ①②③④
7 ①②③④	37 ①②③④	67 ①②③④	97 ①②③④	127 ①②③④	157 ①②③④
8 ①②③④	38 ①②③④	68 ①②③④	98 ①②③④	128 ①②③④	158 ①②③④
9 ①②③④	39 ①②③④	69 ①②③④	99 ①②③④	129 ①②③④	159 ①②③④
10 ①②③④	40 ①②③④	70 ①②③④	100 ①②③④	130 ①②③④	160 ①②③④
11 ①②③④	41 ①②③④	71 ①②③④	101 ①②③④	131 ①②③④	161 ①②③④
12 ①②③④	42 ①②③④	72 ①②③④	102 ①②③④	132 ①②③④	162 ①②③④
13 ①②③④	43 ①②③④	73 ①②③④	103 ①②③④	133 ①②③④	163 ①②③④
14 ①②③④	44 ①②③④	74 ①②③④	104 ①②③④	134 ①②③④	164 ①②③④
15 ①②③④	45 ①②③④	75 ①②③④	105 ①②③④	135 ①②③④	165 ①②③④
16 ①②③④	46 ①②③④	76 ①②③④	106 ①②③④	136 ①②③④	166 ①②③④
17 ①②③④	47 ①②③④	77 ①②③④	107 ①②③④	137 ①②③④	167 ①②③④
18 ①②③④	48 ①②③④	78 ①②③④	108 ①②③④	138 ①②③④	168 ①②③④
19 ①②③④	49 ①②③④	79 ①②③④	109 ①②③④	139 ①②③④	169 ①②③④
20 ①②③④	50 ①②③④	80 ①②③④	110 ①②③④	140 ①②③④	170 ①②③④
21 ①②③④	51 ①②③④	81 ①②③④	111 ①②③④	141 ①②③④	171 ①②③④
22 ①②③④	52 ①②③④	82 ①②③④	112 ①②③④	142 ①②③④	172 ①②③④
23 ①②③④	53 ①②③④	83 ①②③④	113 ①②③④	143 ①②③④	173 ①②③④
24 ①②③④	54 ①②③④	84 ①②③④	114 ①②③④	144 ①②③④	174 ①②③④
25 ①②③④	55 ①②③④	85 ①②③④	115 ①②③④	145 ①②③④	175 ①②③④
26 ①②③④	56 ①②③④	86 ①②③④	116 ①②③④	146 ①②③④	176 ①②③④
27 ①②③④	57 ①②③④	87 ①②③④	117 ①②③④	147 ①②③④	177 ①②③④
28 ①②③④	58 ①②③④	88 ①②③④	118 ①②③④	148 ①②③④	178 ①②③④
29 ①②③④	59 ①②③④	89 ①②③④	119 ①②③④	149 ①②③④	179 ①②③④
30 ①②③④	60 ①②③④	90 ①②③④	120 ①②③④	150 ①②③④	180 ①②③④

INSTRUCTIONS

- Use black lead pencil only (HB).

- Do NOT use ink or ballpoint pens.

- Completely fill the ovals.

- N'utilisez qu'un crayon HB.

- Ne PAS utiliser de stylo.

- Noircissez les ovales complètement.

EXAMPLES/EXEMPLES

Right/Correct

Wrong/Incorrect

- Completely erase any answer you wish to change.

- Do NOT make any stray marks on the answer sheet.

- Do not fold or staple the answer sheet.

COMPLETE THE IDENTIFICATION PORTION OF YOUR ANSWER SHEET

- Print your name, date of birth, date of the examination and name of the examination (from the cover of your test booklet). Fill the oval corresponding to the language of writing.

- Print, in the appropriate boxes, your candidate number, writing centre code, and test form number (from the cover of your test booklet).

- Fill in the corresponding oval for each digit.

- Effacez complètement les réponses que vous voulez changer.

- Ne faites AUCUNE autre marque sur la feuille-réponses.

- Ne pas plier ou agrafer la feuille-réponses.

REMPLISSEZ LA PARTIE RENSEIGNEMENTS DE VOTRE FEUILLE-RÉPONSES

- Inscrivez votre nom, votre date de naissance, la date de l'examen et le nom de l'examen (apparaissant sur la page couverture de votre cahier d'examen). Noircissez l'ovale correspondant à la langue de l'examen.

- Inscrivez, dans les espaces appropriés, le numéro d'identité, le code du centre d'examen, et le numéro du formulaire de l'épreuve (apparaissant sur la page couverture de votre cahier d'examen).

- Noircissez l'ovale correspondant à chaque lettre ou chiffre.

ANSWER SHEET
(See instructions on reverse)

FEUILLE-RÉPONSES
(Voir les instructions au verso)

Family Name - Nom de famille	First Name - Prénom

Date of Birth - Date de naissance	Date of Writing - Date de l'épreuve
DY - JR MO YR - AN	DY - JR MO YR - AN

Test - Épreuve

Language of Writing - Langue	
English ◯	Français ◯

Candidate Number / Numéro d'identité

Writing Centre Code / Code du centre

Test Form / Formulaire

(digit bubbles 1–0 in columns)

1 ①②③④	31 ①②③④	61 ①②③④	91 ①②③④	121 ①②③④	151 ①②③④
2 ①②③④	32 ①②③④	62 ①②③④	92 ①②③④	122 ①②③④	152 ①②③④
3 ①②③④	33 ①②③④	63 ①②③④	93 ①②③④	123 ①②③④	153 ①②③④
4 ①②③④	34 ①②③④	64 ①②③④	94 ①②③④	124 ①②③④	154 ①②③④
5 ①②③④	35 ①②③④	65 ①②③④	95 ①②③④	125 ①②③④	155 ①②③④
6 ①②③④	36 ①②③④	66 ①②③④	96 ①②③④	126 ①②③④	156 ①②③④
7 ①②③④	37 ①②③④	67 ①②③④	97 ①②③④	127 ①②③④	157 ①②③④
8 ①②③④	38 ①②③④	68 ①②③④	98 ①②③④	128 ①②③④	158 ①②③④
9 ①②③④	39 ①②③④	69 ①②③④	99 ①②③④	129 ①②③④	159 ①②③④
10 ①②③④	40 ①②③④	70 ①②③④	100 ①②③④	130 ①②③④	160 ①②③④
11 ①②③④	41 ①②③④	71 ①②③④	101 ①②③④	131 ①②③④	161 ①②③④
12 ①②③④	42 ①②③④	72 ①②③④	102 ①②③④	132 ①②③④	162 ①②③④
13 ①②③④	43 ①②③④	73 ①②③④	103 ①②③④	133 ①②③④	163 ①②③④
14 ①②③④	44 ①②③④	74 ①②③④	104 ①②③④	134 ①②③④	164 ①②③④
15 ①②③④	45 ①②③④	75 ①②③④	105 ①②③④	135 ①②③④	165 ①②③④
16 ①②③④	46 ①②③④	76 ①②③④	106 ①②③④	136 ①②③④	166 ①②③④
17 ①②③④	47 ①②③④	77 ①②③④	107 ①②③④	137 ①②③④	167 ①②③④
18 ①②③④	48 ①②③④	78 ①②③④	108 ①②③④	138 ①②③④	168 ①②③④
19 ①②③④	49 ①②③④	79 ①②③④	109 ①②③④	139 ①②③④	169 ①②③④
20 ①②③④	50 ①②③④	80 ①②③④	110 ①②③④	140 ①②③④	170 ①②③④
21 ①②③④	51 ①②③④	81 ①②③④	111 ①②③④	141 ①②③④	171 ①②③④
22 ①②③④	52 ①②③④	82 ①②③④	112 ①②③④	142 ①②③④	172 ①②③④
23 ①②③④	53 ①②③④	83 ①②③④	113 ①②③④	143 ①②③④	173 ①②③④
24 ①②③④	54 ①②③④	84 ①②③④	114 ①②③④	144 ①②③④	174 ①②③④
25 ①②③④	55 ①②③④	85 ①②③④	115 ①②③④	145 ①②③④	175 ①②③④
26 ①②③④	56 ①②③④	86 ①②③④	116 ①②③④	146 ①②③④	176 ①②③④
27 ①②③④	57 ①②③④	87 ①②③④	117 ①②③④	147 ①②③④	177 ①②③④
28 ①②③④	58 ①②③④	88 ①②③④	118 ①②③④	148 ①②③④	178 ①②③④
29 ①②③④	59 ①②③④	89 ①②③④	119 ①②③④	149 ①②③④	179 ①②③④
30 ①②③④	60 ①②③④	90 ①②③④	120 ①②③④	150 ①②③④	180 ①②③④

INSTRUCTIONS

- Use black lead pencil only (HB).

- Do NOT use ink or ballpoint pens.

- Completely fill the ovals.

- N'utilisez qu'un crayon HB.

- Ne PAS utiliser de stylo.

- Noircissez les ovales complètement.

EXAMPLES/EXEMPLES

Right/Correct

Wrong/Incorrect

Writing Centre Code
Code du centre

| 1 | 1 | – | 1 | 1 | 2 |

Writing Centre Code
Code du centre

| 1 | 1 | – | 1 | 1 | 2 |

- Completely erase any answer you wish to change.

- Do NOT make any stray marks on the answer sheet.

- Do not fold or staple the answer sheet.

- Effacez complètement les réponses que vous voulez changer.

- Ne faites AUCUNE autre marque sur la feuille-réponses.

- Ne pas plier ou agrafer la feuille-réponses.

COMPLETE THE IDENTIFICATION PORTION OF YOUR ANSWER SHEET

- Print your name, date of birth, date of the examination and name of the examination (from the cover of your test booklet). Fill the oval corresponding to the language of writing.

- Print, in the appropriate boxes, your candidate number, writing centre code, and test form number (from the cover of your test booklet).

- Fill in the corresponding oval for each digit.

REMPLISSEZ LA PARTIE RENSEIGNEMENTS DE VOTRE FEUILLE-RÉPONSES

- Inscrivez votre nom, votre date de naissance, la date de l'examen et le nom de l'examen (apparaissant sur la page couverture de votre cahier d'examen). Noircissez l'ovale correspondant à la langue de l'examen.

- Inscrivez, dans les espaces appropriés, le numéro d'identité, le code du centre d'examen, et le numéro du formulaire de l'épreuve (apparaissant sur la page couverture de votre cahier d'examen).

- Noircissez l'ovale correspondant à chaque lettre ou chiffre.

ANSWER SHEET
(See instructions on reverse)

FEUILLE-RÉPONSES
(Voir les instructions au verso)

Family Name - Nom de famille	First Name - Prénom

Date of Birth - Date de naissance	Date of Writing - Date de l'épreuve
/ / DY - JR MO YR - AN	/ / DY - JR MO YR - AN

Test - Épreuve

Language of Writing - Langue	
English ○	**Français** ○

Candidate Number / Numéro d'identité

Writing Centre Code / Code du centre

Test Form / Formulaire

1 ①②③④   31 ①②③④   61 ①②③④   91 ①②③④   121 ①②③④   151 ①②③④
2 ①②③④   32 ①②③④   62 ①②③④   92 ①②③④   122 ①②③④   152 ①②③④
3 ①②③④   33 ①②③④   63 ①②③④   93 ①②③④   123 ①②③④   153 ①②③④
4 ①②③④   34 ①②③④   64 ①②③④   94 ①②③④   124 ①②③④   154 ①②③④
5 ①②③④   35 ①②③④   65 ①②③④   95 ①②③④   125 ①②③④   155 ①②③④
6 ①②③④   36 ①②③④   66 ①②③④   96 ①②③④   126 ①②③④   156 ①②③④
7 ①②③④   37 ①②③④   67 ①②③④   97 ①②③④   127 ①②③④   157 ①②③④
8 ①②③④   38 ①②③④   68 ①②③④   98 ①②③④   128 ①②③④   158 ①②③④
9 ①②③④   39 ①②③④   69 ①②③④   99 ①②③④   129 ①②③④   159 ①②③④
10 ①②③④   40 ①②③④   70 ①②③④   100 ①②③④   130 ①②③④   160 ①②③④
11 ①②③④   41 ①②③④   71 ①②③④   101 ①②③④   131 ①②③④   161 ①②③④
12 ①②③④   42 ①②③④   72 ①②③④   102 ①②③④   132 ①②③④   162 ①②③④
13 ①②③④   43 ①②③④   73 ①②③④   103 ①②③④   133 ①②③④   163 ①②③④
14 ①②③④   44 ①②③④   74 ①②③④   104 ①②③④   134 ①②③④   164 ①②③④
15 ①②③④   45 ①②③④   75 ①②③④   105 ①②③④   135 ①②③④   165 ①②③④
16 ①②③④   46 ①②③④   76 ①②③④   106 ①②③④   136 ①②③④   166 ①②③④
17 ①②③④   47 ①②③④   77 ①②③④   107 ①②③④   137 ①②③④   167 ①②③④
18 ①②③④   48 ①②③④   78 ①②③④   108 ①②③④   138 ①②③④   168 ①②③④
19 ①②③④   49 ①②③④   79 ①②③④   109 ①②③④   139 ①②③④   169 ①②③④
20 ①②③④   50 ①②③④   80 ①②③④   110 ①②③④   140 ①②③④   170 ①②③④
21 ①②③④   51 ①②③④   81 ①②③④   111 ①②③④   141 ①②③④   171 ①②③④
22 ①②③④   52 ①②③④   82 ①②③④   112 ①②③④   142 ①②③④   172 ①②③④
23 ①②③④   53 ①②③④   83 ①②③④   113 ①②③④   143 ①②③④   173 ①②③④
24 ①②③④   54 ①②③④   84 ①②③④   114 ①②③④   144 ①②③④   174 ①②③④
25 ①②③④   55 ①②③④   85 ①②③④   115 ①②③④   145 ①②③④   175 ①②③④
26 ①②③④   56 ①②③④   86 ①②③④   116 ①②③④   146 ①②③④   176 ①②③④
27 ①②③④   57 ①②③④   87 ①②③④   117 ①②③④   147 ①②③④   177 ①②③④
28 ①②③④   58 ①②③④   88 ①②③④   118 ①②③④   148 ①②③④   178 ①②③④
29 ①②③④   59 ①②③④   89 ①②③④   119 ①②③④   149 ①②③④   179 ①②③④
30 ①②③④   60 ①②③④   90 ①②③④   120 ①②③④   150 ①②③④   180 ①②③④

INSTRUCTIONS

- Use black lead pencil only (HB).

- Do NOT use ink or ballpoint pens.

- Completely fill the ovals.

- N'utilisez qu'un crayon HB.

- Ne PAS utiliser de stylo.

- Noircissez les ovales complètement.

EXAMPLES/EXEMPLES

Right/Correct

Writing Centre Code
Code du centre

1 1 – 1 1 2

Wrong/Incorrect

Writing Centre Code
Code du centre

1 1 – 1 1 2

- Completely erase any answer you wish to change.

- Do NOT make any stray marks on the answer sheet.

- Do not fold or staple the answer sheet.

- Effacez complètement les réponses que vous voulez changer.

- Ne faites AUCUNE autre marque sur la feuille-réponses.

- Ne pas plier ou agrafer la feuille-réponses.

COMPLETE THE IDENTIFICATION PORTION OF YOUR ANSWER SHEET

- Print your name, date of birth, date of the examination and name of the examination (from the cover of your test booklet). Fill the oval corresponding to the language of writing.

- Print, in the appropriate boxes, your candidate number, writing centre code, and test form number (from the cover of your test booklet).

- Fill in the corresponding oval for each digit.

REMPLISSEZ LA PARTIE RENSEIGNEMENTS DE VOTRE FEUILLE-RÉPONSES

- Inscrivez votre nom, votre date de naissance, la date de l'examen et le nom de l'examen (apparaissant sur la page couverture de votre cahier d'examen). Noircissez l'ovale correspondant à la langue de l'examen.

- Inscrivez, dans les espaces appropriés, le numéro d'identité, le code du centre d'examen, et le numéro du formulaire de l'épreuve (apparaissant sur la page couverture de votre cahier d'examen).

- Noircissez l'ovale correspondant à chaque lettre ou chiffre.

64397

THE CANADIAN PN/NA EXAM PREP GUIDE

SATISFACTION SURVEY

Your opinion is important to help us improve future editions of the *Canadian PN/NA Exam Prep Guide* and to better meet the needs of PN/NA students. Please complete the following questionnaire, and mail or fax to the Canadian Nurses Association (see address and fax number at bottom of page 2). Your responses will be treated with complete confidentiality. Please fill in the circle corresponding to your response.

A. PREP GUIDE CONTENT

Please rate the following aspects of the *Prep Guide* content:

	Poor	Fair	Average	Good	Excellent
1. Background on the PN/NA Exam	O	O	O	O	O
2. Test-taking strategies	O	O	O	O	O
3. Practice exam	O	O	O	O	O
4. Score interpretation of the practice exam	O	O	O	O	O
5. Performance profile	O	O	O	O	O
6. Answer rationales	O	O	O	O	O
7. Classification of questions (in Rationales and Performance Profile)	O	O	O	O	O
8. References	O	O	O	O	O
9. Overall content of the *Prep Guide*	O	O	O	O	O
10. Overall usefulness of the *Prep Guide* in helping you prepare for the PN/NA Exam	O	O	O	O	O

COMMENTS / SUGGESTIONS: _____

_____

B. PREP GUIDE FORMAT

Please rate the following aspects of the *Prep Guide* format:

	Poor	Fair	Average	Good	Excellent
1. Overall size and length of the *Prep Guide*	O	O	O	O	O
2. Type of binding	O	O	O	O	O
3. Organization/layout of the *Prep Guide*	O	O	O	O	O

COMMENTS / SUGGESTIONS: _____

_____

64397

THE CANADIAN PN/NA EXAM PREP GUIDE

C. PREP GUIDE MARKETING

1. How did you hear about the *Prep Guide*?
   - ○ ADVERTISEMENT
   - ○ OTHER STUDENTS
   - ○ FLYER
   - ○ OTHER: _____
   - ○ POSTER
   - ○ INSTRUCTOR
   - ○ BOOKMARK

2. Where did you purchase the *Prep Guide*?
   - ○ SCHOOL BOOKSTORE   ○ CNA MAIL ORDER   ○ OTHER: _____

3. How much did you pay (not including taxes) for the *Prep Guide*?   ○ $39.95   ○ OTHER: _____
   Do you think this is reasonable?   ○ YES   ○ NO

4. Did you use any other exam practice book(s), in addition to *The Canadian PN/NA Exam Prep Guide*?
   - ○ YES   ○ NO

   If yes, which did you prefer?

   - ○ CANADIAN PN/NA EXAM PREP GUIDE   ○ OTHER (please specify): _____

5. What do you plan to do with your copy of the *Prep Guide* after you have written the PN/NA Exam?
   - ○ KEEP IT
   - ○ SELL IT
   - ○ GIVE IT AWAY
   - ○ OTHER _____

6. Who are you?   ○ STUDENT   ○ TEACHER   ○ OTHER: _____

D. GENERAL COMMENTS

(Include any other services or products you feel would be beneficial to PN/NA students.)

_____

_____

_____

THANK YOU FOR COMPLETING THIS SURVEY.

Please send this completed survey by mail or by fax to:

Canadian Nurses Association
Testing Division
50 Driveway, Ottawa ON K2P 1E2
FAX: (613) 237-3520